Ragman's City

Ragman's City

BY BORIS SIMON

Translated by Sidney Cunliffe-Owen

Coward-McCann, Inc.   New York

To the memory of

DOCTOR REBUFFAT

*and his comrades of Emmaus
who like him died at their post*

AND

*To all those who continue to strive
for the same infallible cause*

CONTENTS

ILLUSTRATIONS

PART ONE

DEEP WINTER

SHOULD THE OCCASION ARISE . . .

THEY WERE all men of goodwill. But the Council had been in session since 3 p.m. They had hoped to reach a decision on this wearisome motion, at whatever cost, before midnight . . . and it was now 1.30 a.m. After seventy-two amendments the President announced yet another one, proposed by State Councillor Léo Hamon.

The latter was on his feet and was about to speak. The atmosphere was stuffy, overheated. The big lamps inside the chandeliers round the semicircle and along the colonnade bordering the gallery left no corner of the hall in shadow and cast a crude light on the grey faces. The hall was decorated like a miniature and very luxurious theatre. There was gilding everywhere, the seats were purple velvet, the columns white marble, statues stood in niches on either side of the mahogany tribunal, and the ceiling was adorned with a vast allegorical design.

The performance had not drawn a large public: only about sixty senators were present. A debate on reconstruction does not lend itself to impassioned argument or to the clash of ideas, as does a debate on war, for instance. It is more a question for technicians. All the amendments proposed so far had been overloaded with a mass of figures. But with Léo Hamon's amendment the feeling suddenly changed, for he dared to talk about the nation's permanent state of sin with regard to the dispossessed.

It was at that moment that all these men responsible for the welfare of the nation, the President on his high seat, the ministers on their benches, the senators in the rows behind them, the handful of spectators in the gallery, the ushers, secretaries and journalists, had looked up with expressions of surprise and annoyance, and turned their heads towards the man who was thus challenging them.

They were well aware that this intervention would prolong the already exhausting session by another half-hour or perhaps longer. The temperature in the hall was around 70 degrees while outside the thermometer in the guardroom showed below freezing and was still falling. A wind had got up with the coming of the night. The senators' chauffeurs had spread rugs over the bonnets of the cars drawn up in the courtyard, and had then gone off to await the end of the session in the little cafés of the Place de l'Odéon.

The gale howled through the forest of Pomponne. A dog whined unceasingly in its kennel beside the Poriet family's shack. Little Luce woke up in the cupboard-bed where she slept with her sister Danielle and her brother Henri. She listened to the groans of the dog tortured by cold and the child felt her tears coming.

'Poor Bobi, please be quiet . . .'

She wanted to get out of bed but was afraid her father would wake up and scold her.

In the flat country round Saint-Ouen an old woman in a wooden lean-to at the bottom of a little garden trembled, her eyes wide open. She felt the cold penetrating to the marrow of her bones, and could not move. Near the embankment of the Ceinture line, inside an old bus, the cry of a baby in its cradle-pram awoke its mother. The gaps in the planks nailed to the window let in a draught. She got up again and rolled up another dishcloth and pushed it underneath the crack to keep out the wind which was attacking the pram from all sides. Outside, a loose strip of corrugated iron tapped against the thin three-ply walls. She pulled the pram softly against the bed. She took her pillow and laid it on the thin eiderdown. The child, warmer now, stopped shivering and groaning and was soon asleep.

Mother, child, old woman—they little knew that their fate was being discussed in Council that night.

The text of the amendment laid before the Assembly by Léo Hamon had been drawn up by the Abbé Pierre, who had once belonged to the same parliamentary group, with the help of a technical expert from the Ministry of Reconstruction. What was it about? Its object was to appropriate out of the ninety milliards set aside for reconstruction one milliard francs for immediate emergency building for the homeless.

As early as December the 12th a newspaper had published the following brief text, preceded by an optimistic article:

'Public Authority has been much moved by the condition of the homeless. Not merely has it been stirred in its feelings, but appears at last to have made up its mind to eliminate the shantytowns from our suburbs, to reduce their dreadful poverty.' Gérard Marin ended his article: 'I hope that Members of Parliament will remember these facts when they are asked in a few days' time to give a roof to those who have none.'

The atmosphere, after a whole day of debate, was beginning to oppress them. Everyone was anxious to get home for the New Year's Eve festivities.

Speaking in his clear and even voice which seemed deliberately to play down the pathetic nature of his text in order to make his subject more convincing, Léo Hamon explained the vital necessity of his amendment. Dark and slight, this man, one of the youngest State Councillors in France, conjured up to his older colleagues a vision of the interminable procession of people queueing outside town halls and city halls in quest of what was their right, because it was indispensable to life itself, a corner where their family, their children, could live . . . and which nobody could give them.

Below him on the Front Bench, the Minister sat with folded arms nodding his head in agreement. He knew all about the problem now being explained. He knew also how powerless even an elected Minister was to meet these requests, these supplications from families at the end of their tether. He had written letters of recommendation to the departments concerned. He had done so in a spirit of disillusion, of scepticism, simply to keep a little hope alive in the supplicants. He had transmitted to them the invariable reply: 'We note your recommendation which will be implemented as soon as there is space available.'

Every Member of Parliament, during the course of his career, had received such heart-rending letters. They listened in silence, leaning their heads on their hands, or clutching abstractedly their sheaves of papers. They, too, knew the whole story already. They, too, had transmitted requests to various departments. And they had never had a letter back to say that any request had been granted. They had done their best. Who was responsible? The ministers who had followed one another during the last ten years had done their best 'so far as in them lay'. The present Minister, who had inherited this accumulation of headaches, also wanted to do his best; but what had happened to the families whose 100,000 dossiers, imploring help, lay in the office files? Were they dead or alive? Where were they? Some were scattered, others were lying in cellars, crammed into caravans, crouching under canvas.

One family of five had been camping in a tent in the forest of St. Germain since September. They had been trying in vain to get a roof over their heads for three years. The autumn had been a mild one. The winter had, at first, been quite bearable. Then, one night, the great cold suddenly came. The father could not sleep. He was thinking of his seventeen-year-old daughter, Anne, who had been away for a fortnight now. He had said nothing to the police, for wherever she was she was better off than here. He did not know that his wife was also awake. Both of them lay on the straw without moving and listened to the breathing of the other two children and to the flapping noise of the canvas against the tent-pole as the wind shook it. Beyond the clearing the trees were crackling in the frost. The mud round the tent hardened. The water in the bucket became a block of ice.

There was now less concentration on what he was saying. It was 2 a.m. The Minister bent his heavy head, the head of a worthy citizen, over his notes, preparing his reply. His face shining with perspiration, Léo Hamon said:

'Our familiarity with this situation, Mr. Minister, must not allow us to forget that it is tragic. How are we to find homes in these circumstances of overpopulation? But what physical and moral catastrophes are the result of *not* finding them! When three, four, five, six people have to live in one room a newborn child is not a joy but a worry, an added burden.

'Any country which permits this state of affairs to exist for hundreds and thousands of families is—and I am speaking purely from the moral aspect—"in a permanent condition of mortal sin" in respect of all those to whom it should ensure at least a home and a chance of happiness.'

He then quoted the Abbé Pierre:

'A priest who was once a Member of Parliament uttered the following sentences which I in turn make my own, denouncing all of us here in this hall: Which of us who pride ourselves on having a certain self-respect would retain as much dignity and virtue as these unfortunate people have done, if he had to live in such conditions?' They think to themselves: '*We* would, anyway', and hope and pray that the speech will soon be over. Some yawn furtively. 'What about the wretched man who followed one of his hovel neighbours to the graveside and said ruefully: "He's got more room dead than he had alive. His coffin is bigger than the space he had in a room where eight people slept." '

There were disapproving frowns here and there. On one of the benches of the Right a senator bent towards his neighbour and whispered: 'Léo Hamon has lost his sense of humour tonight.' His neighbour answered: 'All this pathetic business is almost in

bad taste.' The President looked at his watch. It was 2.15 a.m.
The speaker's voice grew louder, sharper.

'I am not talking just for the dismal pleasure of recalling de-
pressing facts, but because we here, in the majesty and panoply of
this legislative Chamber, *must* become aware of this human drama.
This is the sombre background to our debates and we must try to
find some solution which will fit the urgency of the problem.'

'Urgent' is a disagreeable word in politics. Parliament works
along historic lines. It takes the long view. Nothing is improvised. Each decision may have such far-reaching consequences
that it deserves studying by committees and departments. What
is three or six months against a background of history?

Now he had reached the heart of the matter. He explained why,
through the years, construction had been slow and the acquisition
of property denied to lean purses. The buildings erected, even
those under the existing plan, were ambitious in character and
expensive to maintain.

'The more building is undertaken—and how little it is—the
more the houses erected are beyond the means of these unfortunate
people. I maintain that this Assembly would incur the maximum
degree of civic wrath and moral condemnation if it refused to concern itself with any family which had less than 200,000 francs in
the bank.' (Applause from the Left and extreme Left.)

The President: 'You have considerably exceeded the time limit
and I must ask you to conclude.'

At about 2 a.m. the wind subsided and it began to snow. The
gale from the north-east laid a blanket of powdery snow over the
forest of Pomponne, on the shanty-town with its caravans, its
huts, its tents. Then it reached the Réserve, and the roofs of the
Champs Fleuris. It beat a tattoo on the tarpaulin of the Bréguets'
bus and on the corrugated-iron roofs of the Passage Félix. It
enveloped Paris, the snow lying hard and fine-grained on the
porch of the Luxembourg Palace and on the senators' cars protected by their rugs.

The President told Léo Hamon to stop. He concluded:

'I suggest practical help in the form of a much more simple type of construction, which would enable the more unfortunate families to be housed immediately, pending the building of more permanent homes.

'There is scope for an interim type of house, immediately habitable, accessible to all, even the poorest, coming half-way between the permanent home which naturally remains our ultimate aim and the squalid cabins of these districts which are not habitations but a horrible collection of bare shelters . . .'

At this point the President interrupted:

'May I point out that there is not only a housing crisis but a speech-making crisis?'

There were smiles. Tired heads were raised in acknowledgment of the President's small joke. The speeches ended with some words of the Abbé Pierre: 'As well as building permits there should be permits to live.'

At last he sat down, wiping his forehead with his handkerchief. The Minister rose, some notes in his hand. Large and calm, he spoke very quietly, with a slight Alsatian accent. Facing Léo Hamon he assured him that the Ministry was paying attention to the question of homes at low rentals in the Parisian districts.

'We have, in fact, built perhaps too few houses at low rentals in Paris in the past. I don't know the why or wherefore, but we have now got to go on with it quickly.'

He sat down and the President read the text of the amendment.

'From the sum of ninety milliards granted for 1954 towards work in connection with implementing the legislation in respect of houses at low rentals, the sum of at least one milliard shall be set aside for the construction of emergency buildings', followed by the means whereby this should be done.

Léo Hamon stood up again and replied to the brief intervention of the Minister.

'In my opinion, your arrangements are totally inadequate to deal with this agonizing problem. I agree that you have men-

tioned societies for building cheap houses, but that is a very long-
term affair. The situation which I have just described requires
immediate attention. One milliard would build 8,000 emergency
shelters quickly. We cannot remain inactive. We can no longer
exercise patience. They can wait no longer.'

It was his last word. He sat down once more. There was a few
seconds' pause in the proceedings while everything hung in the
balance, while the fate, the life or death, of thousands of men,
women and children was being decided in silence. Then it all
began to move fast.

The Chairman of the Committee, when questioned by the
President, was not unfavourably disposed, but afraid of improvisation; he requested an adjournment. The Committee would
make a detailed study of the problem. It was for the Minister to
decide. Everyone showed goodwill but all were tied by this fear
of improvisation, bogged down in this cardinal sin of French
political life—prudence. Thousands of prudent actions, small
hesitations, stalling postponement, demands for more detailed
study, promises to go into the question more thoroughly; thousands of refusals to accept responsibility, thousands of small acts
of cowardice by individuals, which coalesce and harden into a
block as heavy as a tombstone.

On the concrete floor of a casemate, part of the old fortifications near the Versailles Gate, Bernard and Jeannette, married
during the summer, cling close to one another. In the underground depth, safe in their mutual young love, they sleep in each
other's arms. When they wake they will swear that time will
reduce this concrete floor to dust sooner than that their love will
fade. They do not know that no noble feeling, no ideal, no
passion, can resist the daily nibbling of poverty, the arch-
destroyer.

In a hut in Norcy a mother woke up suddenly. The silence
woke her. It was no longer snowing. There was no wind. It was
completely quiet. She listened, passing her hand gently over the

face of the six-months-old child in its packing-case beside the bed. She felt the light breath on her fingers. She thought of getting up and warming up a hot bottle, but the water in the bucket was a block of ice. So she took the child and slipped the little body with the frozen hands in between herself and her husband in the narrow bed. The child moaned, a feeble, bird-like sound. She pressed it to her breast to warm it; she could hear its small heart beating. She stayed awake for a long time shivering, but at last she managed to go to sleep again. Outside was the black silence of the night.

The President: 'What is the Government's opinion?'

The Minister rose once more. He recalled the importance that his Ministry attached to this question.

'There exists a whole sector of French families who have no home worthy of the name. I said just now that the best way to solve this problem was to build fast. This requires consideration, as the Chairman of the Committee pointed out. We could not earmark one milliard francs to build houses at low rentals which would not fulfil the requirements of the law. We must work out a formula. I promise Monsieur Hamon that this will be done. We must come to an understanding as to the degree of comfort to be provided and also as to the time factor.'

Was not that correct? The time factor, the legal requirements, the standard of comfort, the time needed for building? What legal requirements, however, were fulfilled by the carcass of a motor-bus, a bridge, a porch, a corner of a courtyard, where these cramped bodies were sheltering? Men need the ordinary require-ments of life to live. As regards comfort they need enough warmth to enable them to last till morning. And the normal duration of a human life. It was time to stop. It was 3.15 a.m.

The President: 'Is the amendment carried?'

Léo Hamon spoke for the last time:

'I want to ask you if, taking into consideration your mistrust of improvisations, you cannot, in the circumstances, accept my amendment on condition that the following words in the first paragraph are omitted: "shall be earmarked", and replaced by "can be earmarked"?'

The Chairman of the Reconstruction Committee:

'No, we cannot do so.'

The Minister: 'I wish to speak.'

The President: 'You have the floor.'

Minister: 'I ask you to withdraw your amendment. I guarantee, for I agree with you, that your observations will not become a dead letter. We have set out along the road that you envisage and we will go along it together if you desire.'

M. Léo Hamon: 'I wish to speak.'

President: 'Monsieur Hamon has the floor.'

M. Hamon: 'I withdraw my amendment with the hope that, should the occasion arise, it will be used as a basis for legislation as soon as the preliminary inquiry has been completed.'

The occasion arose. A child had just died.

2

AT A CHILD'S FUNERAL

THE MAN seemed very upset . . .

I heard about it from Charles, the night-watchman. The story is extraordinary, but very simple.

He was big and strong, almost a giant. He wore a black over-coat, and marched along the pavement between two of his friends, just in front of Charles, who was bringing up the rear of the pro-cession with Lucien. There were some thirty following the child's coffin. The Abbé Pierre went in front, reciting the prayers, to the responses of the Indo-Chinese, who was acting as his server. The loud voice of Jean Pierre led the recital of the Rosary. It was ten years since Charles had said it. It came back to him at once. He asked Lucien who the man was, a journalist perhaps, but Lucien did not know either who the big fellow was. They had noticed his black car negotiating the narrow Passage Félix. The chauffeur got down and opened the door and the Abbé Pierre, who was getting out of his own small car at the same moment, went up to him, whispering: 'It is here.'

Slithering about in the mud, blackened by coke from the gas-works, they approached the motor-bus, but the small body had been taken to the brick-and-plaster lean-to, at the bottom of the little garden, behind the vehicle. The undertakers nailed down the lid, lifted the coffin, which was no bigger than a violin-case, and put it outside.

'Maybe it's the Mayor,' Lucien whispered. It was cold, and a bitter wind penetrated through their coats. Charles had a touch of 'flu; he put on his hat again, and turned up the collar of his windjacket. But the big man remained bareheaded. It was a large, round, officer-type head or, at any rate, the head of someone in authority, and a man of the North, or perhaps an Alsatian. His skin was red with cold, his stubborn face wore an expression so worried and tense that Charles thought he must belong to the family. But if that were the case, why was he not walking with the child's parents? Nobody was aware that this poverty-stricken family had middle-class relatives. Charles noticed that his mud-stained shoes were made of good leather and had been well polished. The bottoms of his well-creased, black trousers were also muddy. He walked with long heavy strides. He was swinging a black felt hat in one hand. He was the only one entirely dressed in black; the only one in regulation mourning. Charles kept wondering why he, who was so clearly not one of them, had come. 'Could it be the Prefect?' Lucien whispered this time. But what would the Prefect be doing at the funeral of a child from 'Thistle Town'?

The oddity of the presence of this personage was accentuated by a bevy of journalists who followed, sometimes running ahead with their cameras, and kneeling down by the roadside to take a picture. But throughout the proceedings, the big man just walked on, looking straight ahead, with neither pride nor shame. He towered over the whole procession.

Charles told me this as it happened, and you could tell how impressed he was; he felt it was a privilege to be walking along with this important person. But in point of fact nobody much impressed the men of Emmaus, where all sorts were to be seen: journalists, friends of the Abbé Pierre, who was once an M.P. himself, even ex-Ministers. What did it matter to them? They were free men; they could look anyone in the face, because they depended on no one, and worked for themselves. Sometimes one got the impression that it was the visitors to Emmaus and the Réserve, who were as shy as little boys in their presence, that it was they who for some reason felt honoured by the welcome given them by the ragpickers.

One day, the Prefect appeared unexpectedly at the workshop. The fellow in charge told him that entry was forbidden.

'But I am the Prefect.'

'O.K.,' came the reply, 'but this isn't a brothel.'

As they were traversing the cross-roads, at the entrance to the little town, where the road became a street between houses, dogs began to bark behind the garden gates. Lucien dug Charles with his elbow and winked at him to turn round. The black car was following fifty yards behind. It had been quietly following them all the way from Thistle Town. It was no longer Lucien and Charles at the tail of the procession, but the mystery vehicle. It made Charles feel uneasy. The wind froze his back, but the look of the man behind the windscreen froze his insides. Just one of those absurd ideas which a touch of the 'flu will bring to life and render plausible.

Charles continued:

'I said that we are free. Morally we are. We relearn at Emmaus to breathe like free men. But there is another kind of freedom, legal freedom. I was well aware that in the procession, just in front of me in fact, walked one of the boys who had been banished.[1] There was another on the run for theft. The heavy overcoat, just in front of me, which cut off the view, those three silent men, and above all, the black car behind us: what did it all mean? I know that if the police had wanted to arrest one of us, things would have happened quite differently. Police would not have followed the child's coffin on foot, for over a mile, in an icy wind. They would have acted at the start, at the same time respecting the dead.

'All these thoughts of mine were ridiculous, as I well knew, but I could not get rid of the anxiety I felt at being wedged there, between the coffin and the black car. I felt as if the whole Emmaus team, into whose ranks these three strangers had insinuated them-

[1] In France, *interdiction de séjour*, banishment from one's home town, is a legal penalty. *Translator.*

selves, was caught in a trap. The nightmare days of the German occupation came back to me. I remembered coming out of the railway station at Villeneuve, one autumn night, with some friends, and finding myself suddenly involved in a raid, caught between a network of soldiers with tommy-guns and the civil police.

'Waiting beside the lorry, into which we were all piled, was the same black car. They let me go next day, but twelve of my comrades never came back.

'I thought of the Abbé Pierre, walking at the head of the procession and protecting us. As long as he who was afraid of nobody was there, we were safe. I thought too of the Cross, carried at the head of the cortège, spreading its peace over us. We were enveloped in a murmur of prayer. I felt calm once more, but sad. At the church, the big man was up in front. The child's mother fainted during the service. When he sprinkled the coffin with holy water, his eyes filled with tears. It was only when we came out of the church that I realized who he was. On the pavement, he shook hands with the Abbé Pierre, who said to him in low tones, for he too was emotionally upset:

' "Thanks for coming."

'The reply was: "I didn't know, I am sorry."

'I could not hear very well, as I was stuck in the group of journalists with their notebooks, in that windy porch. The big man bent towards the Abbé Pierre and said softly that he was an ordinary fellow, like the rest, and a Christian, and that he was greatly upset by this innocent victim.

' "I shall visit your workshops," he said, "and see what can be done." And the Abbé Pierre answered: "Thank you, Mr. Minister, we rely on you." '

Charles now understood all that this meant. He had not yet read the letter, published in the papers, which the Abbé Pierre had written the day following the death of the child during that notorious night when the Council had rejected the demand for credits to build houses to shelter other children.

'It would be a good thing if you could come among us,' the

priest had written. He had come. He had made the gesture. His conscience (for he was a decent man) had imposed on him this painful act of reparation. By attending the funeral, he admitted his share of responsibility. This could harm him with his colleagues, damage his career. He could have answered the priest's letter formally from the Ministry, or ignored it altogether.

'Instead, he had been brave enough to confront us, and to shake hands with the parents. This was something quite new and important, and it shook us. We could now hope that our needs might become realities. We were no longer alone.

'I thought of the child. The coffin was *en route* once more, this time for the cemetery. While the noise of the sabots and the wheels grew fainter, and the procession of family and friends accompanied the child who by its death had obtained this, and so much else, I heard the Minister say to the group of journalists surrounding him: "I don't consider the rejection of Monsieur Hamon's amendment on the subject of the Emergency Cities as a categorical and final refusal—it was submitted to me, after sixty-two others, at the end of an exhausting night session. I was taken unawares. Believe me, we are going to study the text of it most carefully. We shall set ourselves to solving all the numerous problems which arise from it."

'For the first time in my life I believed a politician when he finished off by saying: "We are determined, despite all the difficulties, to bring the matter to a successful conclusion."

'At last we have something to hope for.'

3

THE BIRTH OF A MYTH

T HE POPULARITY of the Abbé Pierre was born that day,
and thenceforward never ceased to grow till it became a
myth. Without scruple, the newspapers, the radio, the
newsreels, seized upon his personality and turned him into a
legend. All France conceived a violent affection for this strange
priest. He, however, kept cool, and tried to preserve his strength.
But he seemed worn out. He sometimes had heart attacks which
forced him to stop talking in the middle of a sentence, his hand
clutched to his breast.

I said to him: 'If you are tired, Father, we will correct the proofs
tomorrow.' 'No,' he answered, 'we must finish them as soon as
possible. Where can we hide ourselves today, so as to have a
little peace?'

At Emmaus he was besieged by telephone, by letter and by
visitors. In his little car we rushed from one end of Paris to the
other, during his few free hours, trying to find a hideout where
he would be forgotten. Sometimes we went to the Champs-de-
Mars, to a small flat belonging to some Sisters of Charity, or to a
hotel bedroom in the Rue de Bourgogne, or to the back room of
a café. He hid from the crowd like a man pursued. Popularity
attached itself to him like a dog which one wants to get rid of,
but which follows one with a doting expression. The myth was
being born, a living monster, full of whims and fancies, which
would devour his time, his energy, his interior peace, his freedom.

He got to know the monster. While his popularity was still

new and not yet obtrusive, he did not mind. He was not yet its captive. He thought it served the cause for which he was working. It was only later that he realized that he himself, and not the work, was the object of this almost idolatrous fervour.

We were driving along behind a bus when one of the occupants, standing on the outside platform, recognized him and told everyone else, and they all peered through our windscreen. But his mind was far away, and he went on driving without noticing; he was not with me at all, driving along at full speed, behind the bus, whose occupants were staring at him. He was far away, having an imaginary interview with the President of the Council, whom he was going to see that day.

He was just going to pass the bus when it slowed down, putting on its brakes so abruptly that he almost hit it. He woke up. 'I wasn't thinking what I was doing,' he said with a quick smile, 'I am always careful about the red lights.' Then: 'They think, you know, that because the Government has taken us up, they can all relax into their well-fed peace—while the Government says: "Since the French people are helping the Abbé to solve his problems, let them get on with it." '

At this moment, a young man jumped down from the bus, which was now stationary, and put his head in through the window. 'Father.' He held out a pile of notes and coins, collected from the passengers in the bus, which moved off. The boy threw the money into the Abbé's lap.

'Excuse me.' He was off, running after the bus.

'Certainly I'll excuse you,' murmured the Abbé, smiling, the money rolling about in his soutane and falling on the floor of the car.

In the small restaurant, all eyes were on him.

'It's the first meal I've had for two days,' he said.

The waitress brought him an anonymous envelope, containing 1,000 francs. Then a young woman came up to the table and without a word, trembling, removed a gold ring, put it down on the tablecloth and went away.

'Yesterday,' he told me, 'I found a 1,000-franc note folded into eight, in the pocket of my windjacket. Somebody slipped it in, in the street. The day before yesterday a beggar came up to me and poured out a handful of money, his day's earnings. And then, there are the notes we get in letters every day. Everyone suddenly feels the need to give.'

'Perhaps their consciences are pricking them?'

'Some, maybe, but not the beggar, or the children, surely—no—they just feel the need to love someone.'

'Yes, and the anti-clerical French people feel the need to love a priest?'

'Quite true. Most priests have let them down. When for once they think they have found the sort they have dreamed about, they hurl themselves upon him.'

He laughed like a schoolboy.

The phenomenon of this spontaneous, anonymous generosity intrigued and also moved him. It meant more than the mere charitable gesture. It indicated a protest, a revolt, a desire for action.

We were sitting in a nice warm drawing-room, in a house on the hill above the Palais de Chaillot. We had taken refuge with some friends, who had hidden him when the Germans put a price on his head. The household, respecting our work, were keeping quiet. From this room we overlooked the city of Paris, as if from a tower.

Armed with red pencils and with pens, we bent over my text.

'You talk here, apropos the setting-up of a depot for children, about the traps laid by the Government for the lower classes. Change that, please—"the lower classes" has a contemptuous sound.'

'No, Father, not in the context.'

'I beg you, do not leave it like that, even if you don't think the phrase harmful. It sounds bad. It always sounds bad in any context. There are no lower classes, we all belong to the people.'

'No, Father, there are lower classes and middle classes.'

He said nothing. He looked down, his face a little taut. A vein swelled in his forehead. I had touched a sensitive nerve. Former indignation was reawakening in him, ancient memories of his days of revolt, when as a young man he first saw the real face of poverty; when he first became aware of his mission, and raged against the lack of understanding of a rich society, where the phrase, 'the lower classes', was used with an inflexion of the voice which one could easily imagine.

'What always gets me is the insistence on splitting up a people into social categories. Classes exist, of course. We live in an age of caste, but that is just why we must urge repeatedly that we form a single unity, with rich people, poor people, all of us, fundamentally human and fundamentally unhappy.'

I resumed the study of the text containing the unlucky phrase.

'Here there is also something to put right. It needs more subtlety in the phrasing. The Government does not wilfully ensnare. This depot for children which is mentioned in the passage we are discussing is at the service of the people. It is useful. What is so maddening is that Public Assistance is only the merest palliative for a profoundly unjust state of affairs. It ought not, in fact, to exist, because a poverty that obliges a young couple to check in a child at the depot, as you check in a suitcase at the left-luggage office, ought not to exist.

'It is therefore a political problem above all, and those who reproach us for putting charity before justice, do not understand us. For us, this distinction does not exist.'

Time was marching on. Night fell. The Abbé had to speak that night at a gala on behalf of the homeless, to be held in one of the big cinemas in the Champs-Élysées. Afterwards, he had to speak again at an At Home, given in a banqueting hall near the Place de la République. He would scarcely have any time to eat.

'Let's get on,' he said. 'You see, one must be careful. Sometimes, without being aware of it, one speaks in accordance with the natural reactions of one's class. "Poor people" and "well-to-

do people", the latter being those who sometimes deign to look
down from their height. A great deal of tact is needed when discussing the sufferings of others.'

In the silence and concentration of our friendly work, time now
seemed to stand still. Sometimes he would get away from the text.
Some word would inspire him to make a long commentary.

'Charity, yes. One is forced to employ this word which nowadays has lost all the strength of the old word *caritas* which was a
virtue, difficult of attainment, but essential and irreplaceable. The
word has become devalued. . . . Ladies of Charity, charitable
works, pity, generosity, fraternity, solidarity. None of these
words emphasizes that relationship in the flesh of all living beings.
I feel in *my* flesh the suffering of *your* flesh, *your* hunger, *your* fear,
your loneliness, and I hate all that makes you suffer, and to deliver
you I will give my life. Fundamentally, like justice, charity
repairs disorders, feels an imperious need to put things back in
place according to the law of life. Let's go back to our manuscript.'

'You must have some food, Father.'

'Yes, yes.'

His face went white, his hand was raised to his chest.

'Are you feeling ill, Father?'

'No, no, I'm all right. Let's get on.'

Turning the pages, he pointed to a line.

'This is also most important. You write, quoting the words of
one of our people: "You can belong to the Right or to the Left,
and be wrong, but when you build houses for mothers, you know
you are infallible!" The beginning of this phrase lacks vigour.
"You can." This seems to say: "It is a matter of indifference
which party you belong to", as if one could take up one's political
standpoint without conviction, even with a lingering doubt. On
the contrary, I believe that one adopts it with the force of one's
whole being. This is very important. Our struggle is political, as
well as charitable. But insist on the necessity, the duty, of acting
through existing institutions. Change the shape of the sentence.
Also change this . . . and this . . . and that.'

I began to feel completely disorganized, and much aware of my shortcomings as a narrator, and my unworthiness as a member of the team in this Emmaus adventure, where the human and the divine, despair and faith, politics and mysticism, the temporary and the eternal, Hell and Salvation, had been linked together for years past. So many had passed through Emmaus, so many fates had been decided, for good or ill. So many tears, so many prayers, so many lives were told in those pages which I held in my hand. Dead leaves from an immense living forest. I tried to tell him this, as I put the pages in order. Others could have done better. I mentioned some names—well-known writers. He stood up, listened with lowered head, and then said:

'It was you I met, and you who came with me.'

He tapped me on the shoulder and smiled.

'Don't worry over your book. It is what it ought to be. And you are the one to write it. You understand that we are being guided. Perhaps you are chosen for this. We will go on with it tomorrow.'

And suddenly his hand gripped the back of the chair. He stood still, leaning forward, holding his breath, as if his heart at the least movement would stop beating.

'Is there anything I can do, Father?'

'No, it will pass.'

But there before me was an old, old man,[1] condemned, resigned, bent beneath an invisible burden. I was afraid. But he slowly recovered and before he had opened his eyes again, the shadow of a smile had passed over his face.

'It's over,' he said, and took a step forward.

It was then that I resolved to write this second book. It is the only way I can fight against the forces which threaten his life.

[1] The Abbé Pierre is in his forties. *Translator.*

4

GALA

O N THE pavement of the Champs-Élysées, beneath the glass and marble façade, with the neon lights above, the crowd was waiting at the entrance to the palatial cinema.

'Hullo, there . . .' The large masculine hand which was held out nonchalantly towards me belonged to Alice, a professor of mathematics, and also a militant communist. Her husband was deported and died in Germany, and since then what was left of her heart belonged to the Party. Winking one dark eye at me, she said: 'I hear you are writing a book about him. What has come over you?'

'Take too long to explain,' I said with a shrug.

She stared at me calculatingly. She was thinking that I was the dupe of my own naïveté, that the growing myth of the Abbé Pierre, created by the capitalists, had seduced me and that I was betraying the cause of the people.

What did the Abbé signify for her? An intelligent priest, a worthy man, but unwittingly pushed on to the stage and manipulated by a reactionary government, to distract people's attention from the real problem, namely the helplessness and rottenness of the régime, and the need for its overthrow.

She fixed me with her dark shrewd eyes. She was longing to find out, quite disinterestedly, my real secret, sordid motive. Or was I just being made a fool of? As we all are, she was thinking, as she viewed the crowd, for 'all Paris' was there, the bourgeoisie, come to pay homage to him who was helping to preserve their privileges. These journalists, those film moguls, all in the pay of capitalism—and the lesser fry, the students—also duped by false sentimentality. This was what she was thinking, and it was no good my arguing with her, for she would win the argument, and end up by accusing me of being more reactionary than ever.

It was on this same pavement, two years before, that the Abbé Pierre had stood alone, in the complete freedom of absolute poverty, distributing to the indifferent crowds his terrible tract, full of revolutionary fire. 'Fear the curse of God and man, you rich. Give all you can, that these despairing, homeless people may exercise their right to live.' He had not changed since then. He was still free. The powers that be would never get a hold over him.

There was a stir. He had arrived in his little car. Photographers flashed their bulbs. The crowd made way, as, limping and exhausted, leaning on a stick, the Abbé entered the glittering hall.

Alice and I went to the Press box. First we saw a newsreel. Then the curtain was lowered, the footlights came on, and in silence the Abbé advanced to the middle of the proscenium. He looked very small, against that immense wall of red velvet in the background. A small solitary figure in black. The footlights threw up weird shadows from the folds of the curtains. There was no microphone, and he had to strain his voice to be heard in that enormous theatre. But he seemed to be out of breath, and only murmured his thanks to the public for giving their contribution to this gala on behalf of the homeless.

He spread open his hands slowly, while the shadows flickered on the draughty curtain.

'The whole nation is in a state of mortal sin. We have been living selfishly—we must no longer be among those who did not realize—who would not save from death men and women like themselves, whose only crime was to be poor. . . . Don't be one of those who would not bother. . . .'

He hurled these last words out at the audience with such force

that faces grew tense and people seemed to shrink into themselves
with shame.

'These men and women,' he went on, 'do not want your
charity; they want the right to live. Justice, not charity, is what
they ask for. We must all pull together, to wipe out this national
shame. Help us, use your influence with the authorities. . . .'

In the stalls, the dress circle, standing on the stairs, two thousand faces were turned towards that grief and anger, watching the
small black figure on the lighted stage. They had not been
spoken to like that before, and it was suddenly brought home to
them that social injustice exists, and that, as the privileged class,
it was their responsibility. He opened his arms, and the vehement
shadows flapped their wings in the curtain folds.

'Help me, my friends,' he cried. 'What can I do by myself,
confronted with so much misery? You who are in a position to
do something, show pity, act justly, so that these desperate people
may recover the right to live!'

Then, more calmly, he added:

'You have heard about the child's death. It is thanks to him
that we are here. But he is not the only one. Other children are
dying of privation and cold at this very minute. Their mothers
and fathers are blaspheming in their despair, and we cannot sleep
peacefully if we think of it, unless we have done something about
it. Give them shelter, a home. They have as much right as any
of us to lead a life of human dignity. Don't leave this place
satisfied because you have made a generous gesture. From this
moment, our real work of rescue starts, and we must be united in
our resolve that such injustice must cease.'

He stopped, leaned down to pick up his stick, and slowly went
back into the wings.

There was silence, and then someone started to clap. Soon the
applause was deafening and continuous.

From now on his enemies could still, in more or less good faith,
accuse him of not completing his work, of causing diversions.
They could not deny that he was the first to pierce the consciences

of the privileged classes with the reality of social injustice! The first to make them shed tears of shame, and realize where their duty lay.

I looked at Alice. She turned to me with a contorted expression on her face and stammered: 'Ah, but it's too easy. . . .'

Then she got up and, as if panic-stricken, fled from the building, jostling her neighbours as she passed.

5

AT POMPONNETTE

FOR A week past, the boy Antoine and big Silvio had formed the crew of the lorry; and the boy enjoyed driving around. He was always on the road, leaving each morning, returning at night to sleep in the dormitory at Emmaus. The lorry did not go to Paris. Its job was to transport all the rags accumulated at Emmaus to the Réserve, which was to be the main warehousing centre. They also carried to the new centre at The Poplars building material and prefabricated parts for huts. There the central offices were to be installed. Sometimes Jean-Pierre would send them to fetch homeless families, either from Paris or from the countryside, to be installed in the recovery centre of Pomponnette.

One day in January I left with them, to bring back to Pomponnette a young couple, with their possessions, from a little village near Coulommiers.

On the way back we let the couple sit in the driver's cabin. Antoine and I were behind with the furniture. It was cold, but on top of his shirt Antoine only wore a sailor's jersey with white and blue stripes. Sitting on a mattress he chain-smoked, staring dreamily at the bare countryside. Suddenly, as we were passing through a village, he pointed to a window where there were some geraniums in a pot.

'My mother loves flowers,' he said. 'We always had some in our room. Red and green—they looked nice against the grey walls.'

Then, with a slight smile on his young face, he looked at me in a way both confident and apprehensive, and said: 'The other night, when I came back to Emmaus, you thought I was drunk, didn't you?'

'And weren't you?'

'Wine doesn't agree with me.'

'You were in a bad way.'

'It wasn't my fault—but I quite see you must have got a bad impression of me.'

He shrugged his shoulders, and then said: 'You haven't by any chance heard if Grégor is back?'

'No.'

'He was one of my pals at Pontault. I hope he's not gone and done something stupid.'

I realized that he had been thinking of his friend all the time. Jean-Pierre and Jacques felt responsible for him, and he felt responsible for Grégor. Thus the chain of friendship linked all the men in our community.

We reached the forest. The lorry turned off the main road. Silvio slowed down on the dirt-track road, which had deep frozen ruts. The load of furniture, shaken to pieces, began to dance all round us with a frightful noise, so much so that I expected the bedside table, perched on the mattress, to come crashing down on my head. My frozen hands clung to the woodwork of the lorry. We were near the end of our journey.

Behind the bare branches of the trees, a huge sombre red sun was setting, and presaging more frost that night. Some ravens flew over, croaking, in a pale green sky of icy purity. A sad smell of wood smoke mingled with the odours from the exhaust. Dogs barked. Slowly, swaying along the central lane of the village, the lorry passed the tumbledown houses, lighted here and there by gasoline lamps. Occasionally blinds were raised, and the shadow of a face was revealed in a rectangle of light. Thereupon, from hovels of beaten earth, or corrugated iron, or planks, from caravans and carcasses of old motor-buses dumped on the ground,

some boys emerged and approached silently to watch the new
inhabitants move in. There wasn't much in the way of distraction
at Pomponnette.

My friend Paulo, who was in charge of the Recovery Centre,
appeared in the headlights, bareheaded, his coat collar up round
his noble monk's face. One of his rare smiles appeared on his thin
lips, a smile lacking in gaiety, when I asked him if he could put
me up for the night.

'Certainly, you can sleep with me, but you don't choose your
moment very well—you evidently don't mind the cold.'

But I did mind it, just as much as he did himself, having spent
ten years in Africa, and besides I was feeling feverish.

The man and woman whom we had transported with their
small possessions had got down from the cabin of the lorry, and
their motionless silhouettes were outlined in the circle of the
lights. Both were young, barely twenty. Only married a week,
they had spent their honeymoon at a hotel in Paris. But a hotel
bedroom is a form of luxury which cannot continue all the year
round, when you only earn twenty-five pounds a month. At
Pomponnette they would be near Paris, where the husband worked
in a brewery. There, they would wait completion in the spring
of the house the men of Emmaus were building for them at
Plessis-Trévise. Utterly exhausted, they were holding hands and
staring in silence at the encampment which was enveloped in a
blue fog from the smoke, at the hovels behind the palisades, at a
broken beech-tree, outlined against the sky and, surrounding it all,
the forest filled with the night. They were trying to summon
up the courage to imprison their life in this desert.

The skinny young man, with the tense features and the sad
eyes, had scarcely opened his mouth throughout the journey,
either when his furniture was being loaded or during the stops
en route. Holding his young wife's hand, with the correct air of
the lower middle class, his expression remained one of anger and
of shame. He did not look at her. He seemed to be begging her
pardon for bringing her there.

Close by, the motionless children contemplated with grave curiosity the faces, distorted with fatigue, of the newcomers. In the middle of the group a little girl of eight or nine years held in her arms a still smaller child, wrapped in a shawl. A twelve-year-old boy, a cigarette in his mouth and wearing a man's trousers far too big for him, had got on to the running-board of the lorry. With a competent air he said to Silvio in the driver's cabin:

'It's a Diesel, isn't it?'

Down the road some bicycle lamps were visible—men coming home from work at Lagny.

From one of the huts a mother called: 'Lucien, Henri!' A dog came up to the couple and sniffed at them mistrustfully.

Then the girl seemed to awake from her torpor. She looked up at her husband and smiled. He too roused himself, took some tobacco out of his pocket, and rolled himself a cigarette. Since he had been unable to find elsewhere the place to which he and his wife had a right, they accepted Pomponnette, and agreed to take the first step in their life together on this frozen mud. Spring would come.

The lorry backed slowly towards the hovel where the rectangle of an open door was outlined in the grey discoloured walls of plaster.

'Pomponnette! It's an odd sort of name,' said the man to his wife, with a bitter sneer. 'I'd imagined something different. Oh well, this is it.'

He turned to Paulo.

'Is that where we have got to go?'

Someone was tugging at my sleeve. It was my friend Luce.

'How is your mother, Luce?'

'She went to the maternity hospital this afternoon,' she whispered.

Silvio had switched off the ignition at last. Antoine jumped down and unhooked the tailboard, which dropped with a crash.

'Off with you, children, and don't be late fetching the water,' cried Paulo.

There was no fountain or well at Pomponnette; the owner of the villa three hundred yards away allowed the inhabitants of the Recovery Centre to use his garden tap from five to six each evening.

'Let's hope the pipe's not frozen,' said Paulo.

The children were not in a hurry to disperse. A woman came out of a neighbouring hovel with a child's pram, in which was a jug. Luce pulled harder at my sleeve.

'I must go,' she said. 'Daddy went off with Mummy, but he may come back tonight. If he doesn't, I shall sleep with Monsieur Paulo. Are you staying?'

'Yes.'

Her face held the ghost of a smile.

I added: 'You have either a little brother or a little sister by this time.'

'Yes,' she said, 'unless . . .'

'Unless what?'

'Mummy was feeling very sick even before they took her away.'

She left me suddenly and scampered off to the deserted house.

'Put the bed here and the table there. Mind—the door is very narrow. You'll have to get it in sideways.'

The hurricane lamp had been hooked to the ceiling, and gradually, piece by piece, the house had been made habitable. The girl had discovered a nail on the wall, and hung a little mirror in a gilded frame on it; the orange reflection of the lamp, in this miniature looking-glass, introduced a note of gaiety.

'It won't be too bad, Marcel, when we get a bit of lino on the floor.'

Marcel said nothing, but closed his lips over his cigarette. He felt too keenly to speak. When they were engaged, he had hoped to be able to offer his young wife another sort of house than this hovel of planks and plaster and beaten earth, in a clearing in the woods; another kind of life from this existence on the fringe of civilization, like savages or outcasts. He felt ashamed, not because of us, but because of her. And he was also angry. Inside himself he knew full well that Emmaus had saved them from the street. For him, as for the others, it would not last. A day would come when all the proletariat in the world would have the right to live a life of human dignity.

But for the moment I sensed in his brusque gestures, his silence, that shame and anger which the forced air of contentment and courage of his wife could not appease, and of his hostility towards us who were helping him. He went to and from the lorry, without opening his mouth, which held the extinct stub of his cigarette.

Suddenly there was nothing left to carry in but an old bicycle tyre, which Silvio's lamp revealed in a corner of the lorry.

'That too?' he asked the young man.

'For heaven's sake—that's done for,' grumbled the latter. 'I told my wife not to bring it.'

He hurled it away. The empty rubber ring flew over the roof of the hovel, towards the stars in the sky, and came to rest hooked to the branches of a thin birch tree.

I heard Silvio laugh and cry out in his weird, half-Polish, half-Italian voice.

'Are you trying to lasso the stars?'

The fire in the little stove had long been out. I could not sleep, I was so cold.

I got out of bed and put on my windjacket. Beside me, Paulo lay asleep, fully clothed, in a large, walnut-wood bed, a bourgeois bed, repaired at Emmaus thoroughly from head to foot, like they did in the old days.

He slept, and dreamed perhaps of Africa, where for ten years he was the director of a mining company. He caught filarosis—hair-thin worms ravaged his athlete's body, lived on his blood, clotted his arteries, made colonies in his muscles, perforated his intestines.

He had undergone a painful and costly treatment in France, from which he had never really recovered. The fall from the gold standard did not help him financially. He did not return to Africa, though all that France could offer him was unemployment, and a bed at Pomponnette.

Luce and her little brother shared a bed at the foot of mine. Their father had not come back. Danielle, the younger sister, had been taken in by a family, into a house already overcrowded with children. Luce's breathing was barely perceptible, but still more fragile must have been the breathing of the newborn child in its incubator. Surgeons, doctors, midwives, nurses, were doing everything to keep the child alive, and perhaps they would succeed. They would then tell the mother that she could take it home. 'Home' at Pomponnette—a hovel of planks and mud and corrugated iron, in the forest, without electricity, but with a lot of frozen mud around. And, but for the shelter of these planks and iron and plaster, it would be the walls of a quay along the river, and for flooring, the street. 'A woman does not bear a child merely so that it shall not die, but so that it shall live.'

'How is it possible?' the Minister of Reconstruction had said repeatedly, on his last visit, the preceding week. 'Why has such a state of affairs been allowed to continue? In the middle of the twentieth century.'

'That is just what I have been asking the public authorities for the last three years,' the Abbé Pierre had replied.

A lady in charge of a Red Cross organization had offered the Abbé five million francs to raze Pomponnette to the ground, and efface this scandal and shame.

'I accept the money,' the Abbé had answered, 'but if I demolish the huts, a couple will arrive off the streets the next day, begging for shelter, and I shall have to build them up again. To destroy Pomponnette would not be to destroy a scandal and a shame, but to add one more disgrace to all those of which Society is guilty in respect of the homeless.'

If he could only last until Easter, Luce's new brother, by then the bad days would have passed, and their little house would be ready for them.

I was aware of a sigh, a yawn, from the bed where Luce and her brother were sleeping. Her face was visible in the gloom.

'Aren't you asleep, Luce?'

'Is Daddy back?'

'I haven't heard him. Go to sleep.'

The face disappeared. She did not move. I hoped she had gone back to sleep.

6

THE GREAT COLD SPELL

THE SNOW began to melt a few days later, and a soft rain made me think the winter was over. Domino said to me: 'Why don't you go back to the South? Your book is finished. What's keeping you?'

I told him about my hopes of its being made into a film, about my meetings with the film agents. But what really kept me was Emmaus. No obligation but friendship.

But the frost returned, and at the end of January down went the thermometer, and the Seine began to freeze over. The sun shone sometimes in the morning, but the east wind never ceased to blow, and its rays did not melt the frost. By midday white clouds filled the sky, and powdery snow began to fall, and was chased by the wind up and down the almost deserted streets.

The Press worked up itself and its readers by recalling the great historic cold spells: neither in 1903 nor in 1917 had the temperature remained so low for so long—and the list of mishaps due to cold filled several columns. Trains were late owing to the freezing of the electric points. Distribution of food was paralysed. The frost and snow disorganized road traffic. The newspapers gave lists of people frozen to death in the streets and in their miserable shacks.

Life in Paris slowed down. Fewer cars in the streets, fewer pedestrians. In a well-known café-restaurant, near the markets, called 'Chez Robert', where the Emmaus crowd used to foregather to eat, the eternal theme was the weather, discussed with an undercurrent of anxiety, disguised by a bantering manner. The proprietor said that the burgundy, brought in casks by lorry, had frozen on the way. We would have to eat it in slices.

The local baker had had to bake by hand in a wood stove, because of the power cuts due to the freezing of the dams down in central France.

And there was no food in the market.

'Did you see the papers? Nine deaths from pneumonia.'

At a factory, a worker went outside, slipped and fell down, and had to be taken to hospital.

'Have you read this? "Unexpected consequences of the cold at Lyon. A military band was unable to play the 'Marseillaise'— vapour froze in the stops and prevented the horns being blown— only the drums were immune."'

The sea at Dunkirk was frozen, and the authorities considered it useless to employ an ice-breaker, as the sea froze solid again behind it. The fishermen came ashore on foot over the ice, leaving their boats, unmanageable because the rigging and ropes were frozen stiff.

And the wolves . . . These quasi-mythical survivals from the Middle Ages appeared in our countryside. In Savoy, fifteen wolves invaded a village and ate a sheep.

'So the wolves are on the way to Paris?'

The man was joking, but the joke did not dissipate the feeling of unease. People lingered indoors, not daring to go out into the windswept streets. Fear descended on the capital, so insulated against all cataclysms. Civilization, like any other living organism, felt itself menaced by the lowering of the temperature by a few degrees. Pipes burst in the houses, central heating went off. Outbreaks of fires increased, due to short circuits and overheating of stoves. Someone tried to thaw a frozen gutter with a blow-lamp, and set fire to his house.

The women did not read the picturesque newspaper stories about the cold spell, and it was a matter of indifference to them if the temperature went to forty below in Norway, while in California there was a heat wave and people were bathing in the sea. They thought about the immediate problems affecting their families, the redoubled anxieties over budgeting, food, clothing, lodging, heating.

'If this goes on, our men won't be able to go to work and the money will run out.'

'If this goes on, transport will be still more erratic, marketing still more difficult, everything scarcer, and therefore dearer.'

'If this goes on, and we can't send our children to school, where they get a free meal at midday, they'll fall ill; we shall have to buy more clothes, more medicines.'

The rich could buy heating like everything else, for warmth is a commodity sold in the form of food, fuel, and strong walls. The poor, in order to economize, stayed in bed or wandered through the shops, or killed time in the pubs. The poorest of all, lacking even the thirty francs necessary to gain them admission to a café or to the platforms of the Underground, collected in ever-increasing numbers above the hot-air vents of the latter.

Not only at night, but also in the daytime, they lay down in heaps in the squares and on the pavements of the boulevards. Huddling together in shivering bunches, they let the snow pile up on their backs.

The crowds hurried past them, these heaps of dying human beings. Hospitals and hostels refused to admit even the sick for lack of room. Men died in the porches of the churches.

This was the moment selected by the Minister of the Interior to distribute to the Préfectures the following circular, advising them to tighten up the orders for evictions:

'As a general rule, you are legally obliged to implement judicial decisions. You should not therefore hesitate to use the powers at your disposal as soon as you are asked to do so by the *Huissier*[1] if

---

[1] There is no exact equivalent in English: a bailiff having police powers. *Translator.*

the latter finds it impossible after repeated attempts to evict unaided.

'The Council of State has ruled that no consideration founded on the necessity of maintaining public order permits the adminis- tration to defer its intervention beyond a reasonable period.

'The impossibility of rehousing the evicted should not of itself be a determining factor in your attitude.

'You should not lose sight of the fact that the non-execution of eviction orders constitutes a grave disturbance of public order, and shows lack of respect for judicial decisions, and therefore for the authority of the State.'

So—solitary old people, couples living on tiny fixed incomes, young couples, were thrown into the street and delivered up to death, in order that the authority of the State should be respected.

The temperature continued to fall, and even the well-clad felt cold. And because they shivered beneath their garments of flan- nel, of thick wool, of fur, even when stepping out of their cars, or through their front doors, they awoke as one man, and allowed themselves to be touched by the appeal of the Abbé Pierre on behalf of the ill-clad and the homeless.

7

TOUR OF THE NIGHT HAUNTS

NINE O'CLOCK in the evening. We were standing outside a music-hall in the Bastille quarter. A Ford Vedette
with a Press badge glided along the narrow street, behind
the Simca Aronde of an M.P. friend of Emmaus, and the Abbé
Pierre's little Citroën.

'Why, there's Druel,' whispered my friend Girard. 'Do you
know him?'

He quoted the name of the Press agency for which this particular journalist worked. I had read several hostile articles by him
about Emmaus, one especially on the squalors of Plessis-Trévise,
echoing certain other newspaper attacks accusing the ragpickers
of being the cause of the outbreak of disease, which was really due
to the tainted water supply for the little community. More
recently, describing a Press conference in a big bar-restaurant in
the Champs-Élysées, when the Abbé Pierre, exhausted and on the
verge of collapsing, had accepted a glass of champagne, Druel had
the effrontery to write: 'In a bar, with a glass of champagne in his
hand, the Abbé Pierre talks about poverty.'

I asked what he had got against the Abbé. 'Is Druel a "fellow-
traveller"?'

'If he were, there would be something to be said for him. No,
Druel is the little fellow who wants to be in the swim, not malicious at heart, but ambitious. He likes to appear tough, and to
knock down what other people respect, just because he thinks that
that is what is meant by being talented, and that that is the way to

"arrive". And his newspaper is really tough. Its style is the so-called "Parisian"—show your teeth and claws, and be entertaining at all costs. Emmaus is something serious which touches people's hearts. That's why it irritates him.'

The Abbé Pierre entered the building by a service door on the left of the large façade. A yellow poster announced the meeting for 9 p.m. The big wrought-iron lamps, hanging from pillars on each side of the main entrance, were not lighted. Groups of people were waiting across the road. A few were coming along from the direction of the Bastille. There was a queue of cars. Stamping our feet on the crisp snow, our breath steaming, we waited for them to open the doors, and talked in low voices in that sombre street. The wind had fallen, but the temperature was still well below zero. My lungs were burning, and the cold gripped my ankles and wrists and temples like a steel ring.

The back door of the Vedette opened, and out got a big fellow, thin, wearing a black overcoat, and bareheaded. He carried a large black bag over his shoulder, bigger than a photographer's apparatus, and came up to us.

'Evening, Girard.'

The latter introduced me to Martel, reporter for the newsreels.

'It's from the *Aurora* that I got the tip,' he said, 'that the Abbé made the tour of the tramps every night. Is it interesting?'

'You'll see after the lecture.'

'I thought of filming a Salvation Army tour, but it has been done twenty times—overdone. The Abbé Pierre is a bit newer stuff.'

Yes, the Abbé Pierre was newer stuff. He was 'good value', as we journalists say, when discussing a subject which 'gives' in the Press. On the movies and the radio, they talk of it 'sticking'. It was no longer a matter of a few tramps to whom a bed was offered, and some soup, and who were left to their perpetual decay thereafter. Since the affair of the dead child and the letter to the Minister, the Abbé represented a new force to which the whole country began to pay attention, not merely the force of a

most moving charity, but the exultant force of a revolt for
justice. That was why he was considered 'good value'.

The very topical problem of the evictions, the numberless victims of the housing shortage and of social misery, had to be
weighed against the plan for the regeneration of each Frenchman,
religiously, politically, morally. Together with his 'community',
the Abbé Pierre defied the optimists by the realities which he
exposed.

The exceptionally cold wave was certainly real enough. The
reporters were on the search for a crop of picturesque images to
describe the two stars of the moment, the Abbé Pierre and the
thermometer.

'Hell's bells,' cried the movie man, 'I'm afraid my flash battery
has run down.'

'Evening, Girard.'

Druel came up to us with his sly, gentle smile: the ironical
demolisher, hunting for the echoes of better men's opinions, pre-
senting the worst aspect of the best things, the weaknesses of great
causes—and why? No reason. To 'arrive'. Perhaps not fundamentally malicious, but the result was the same.

'Tell me, Girard, you know how he organizes these tours of the
tramps. How did it start?'

'He didn't organize anything. It all happened by chance. The
other night he saw some people lying in the street—he gave them
some money to go to a hostel. That's all. The day before yesterday he distributed biscuits and hot coffee.'

'Yes, yes—but is that all?' said Druel. 'It's arranged so that
everyone knows about it, eh? He looks after his publicity all
right. And say—where did he find chaps sleeping out of doors?
A dozen ancient, professional tramps, no more, and who are used
to it. If you offered them a warm room they would prefer the
street.'

'Not only tramps.'

'Tell me, Girard, have you ever come across any young people
lying in the street?'

The tall movie man laughed.

'In case we don't come across any, we've brought some old coats and sacks in the car, and a girl friend to pose with one of us as an evicted young couple, reduced to sleeping on the pavement.'

Druel glanced at the Simca Aronde, parked near us, and noticed the M.P.'s badge.

'So he's invited the Government. Who's this?'

Girard named the M.P.

'Ah, yes, the little sly-boots—jealous of the Minister's popularity, he wants him to come unstuck, no doubt. The Minister's an old fox, too—with his child's funeral—what a coup! Blasted demagogues! All most interesting—charity as the weapon of the political careerists.'

'Oh, go to hell!' cried Girard, out of patience. 'When are they going to open the door?'

Just at that moment, the Abbé Pierre came out of the side door, followed by Domino, loaded with his heavy case of lantern slides in colour which were to illustrate the Abbé's talk.

'The heating's out of order,' said the Abbé. 'The pipes have burst. I can't lecture in an icy hall.'

'What a pity,' murmured a blonde young girl student, contemplating the priest with adoring eyes.

The Abbé noticed Druel and extended his hand, the fog of his breath enveloping the reporter's face.

'Come on, shall I take you round the night spots?'

Druel blinked, and replied in a voice in which impudence and respect were mixed:

'Haven't you got enough troubles already, Father?'

The Salvation Army's barge, its roof whitened by snow, slept on the black water of the Seine. The lamp above the bridge was out. Only the red signal-lights, fore and aft, could still be seen. Having no more room on board, it seemed to be sailing away with its cargo of distressed people, now sleeping peacefully, warm and satisfied. Those who had missed the boat lacked the courage to go searching for another refuge. What was the use?

Girard passed his glove over the car window, which was caked with rime. Through the curtain of snow, we saw the Abbé Pierre's car slow down at the end of the bridge, as if he was hesitating about which way to go. We expected him to turn right, towards the Boulevard St. Germain. It was not late, only 10 p.m. There were few cars, however, on the boulevards and they were crawling along. There was nobody on the pavements.

The Citroën gave a sudden leap forward and at full speed crossed the roundabout in the direction of the Botanical Gardens. The Abbé had spotted the quarry, afar off, and invisible to us. Behind his pilot car swept the procession, the M.P.'s car, our own and Druel's. We accelerated, then abruptly braked screechingly, skidding to a stop on the icy road. Hardly were the cars at rest, bumper to bumper, when journalists, photographers, movie-men, leaped out holding their apparatus like weapons. The car doors slammed briskly. The Abbé was leaning over a shape, piled up like a heap of rags against the white wall of the Botanical Gardens. The Abbé bent down still further, and the wings of his big cape enveloped the thing on the ground. The rest of the company jostled each other to have a look. Hurriedly they tore off their gloves, despite the cold, to focus their cameras.

'My friend,' said the Abbé.

He tapped him on the shoulder, then turning to us, he stood aside and we saw the man. He had pulled his beret over his eyes, on to his ears. All one could see of his face, buried in a blue striped scarf and inside the collar of a greasy raincoat, was a nose and pale cheekbones. His arms folded across his chest, he was trying to keep warm. His fists were clenched. He had rope soles on his feet, while round his ankles and twisted legs he had rolled news-papers, which he had tied on with pieces of string. He had no baggage, not even a stone on which to rest his head against the asphalt. The thing that affected me most about him was not his lack of baggage, his miserable garments, but his loneliness: lost in the cold, this human being leaning against the wall, on the other side of which hyenas and wolves were sheltered.[1] He had no one, neither friend, nor wife, nor dog, to comfort and warm him. Thank heaven, he had ceased to be conscious of his solitude. He slept—or perhaps he was dead.

Lying there beneath those miserable wrappings of newspaper, his head sunk beneath his shoulders, flat to the earth, he seemed quite small, no bigger than a child; and motionless, no signs of respiration. A corpse in the twisted posture of a Mexican mummy.

All of us were still and silent, so that the icy flakes of snow were audible, falling on the newspapers and the old raincoat.

Suddenly there was the light of an arc-lamp. At the abrupt illumination the inert shape seemed to bound into the air in one piece, then fell back on the ground, and we all instinctively recoiled.

'Raise it higher,' came the imperious voice of Martel. His assistant raised the lamp. The inert body was bathed in the intense light of the film projector. The camera began turning, with an oily creaking, and the lens came nearer to the man, passing above the whole length of his body from head to toe, like a machine-gun plastering a corpse.

The movie man was doing his job of filming with complete detachment, as if he himself were only a machine. Light from the arc-lamp shone in all our faces, and I realized that the others felt the same shame as I did. This sense of shame began at this moment and did not leave us. Even Druel looked both ashamed and disgusted.

He was annoyed at being there, and the pretty little blonde student looked suddenly ugly, because of the way her lips were contorted, as if she were paralysed. Then the lights went out, and our dazzled eyes eventually made out the black shape of the Abbé Pierre, once more bending over the man, kneeling by his side,

[1] The Botanical Gardens in Paris contain a zoo. *Translator.*

taking him by the shoulders, wrapping him in the wings of his black cape, restoring him to life.

'Wake up—get up—come on—wake up!' The little blonde put her red-woollen-gloved hands to her mouth and murmured: 'He is dead.'

A voice behind me, Druel's, said: 'He is drunk.'

The man was not dead, but he may have been too drunk to feel the cold. Wine may have saved his life, but the newspapers tied to his legs showed that before losing consciousness he had realized the danger, and that he wished, if not to survive, at any rate not to suffer.

At last he moved. The heavy brown eyelids opened and the head was raised from the ground. Hoisting himself up from the icy pavement with a large grey hand, he sat up, then stretched his legs. He looked at us and mumbled: 'I have my identity papers.'

'It doesn't matter about that,' said the Abbé Pierre, 'but you can't stay here. Go and get warm at an hotel. Here is the money for a room.'

'A room?' repeated the man, his eyes fixed on the 500-franc note which the Abbé was holding out to him.

'He'll get drunk again with it,' said Druel.

'Well, so much the worse—or so much the better!' cried the Abbé in sudden wrath. 'Let him get drunk, if that will keep him alive until tomorrow and help him to forget his suffering.'

Domino had returned to the priest's car and came back with a thermos. He poured some coffee laced with rum into a mug. The man sniffed the alcohol and stretched out his hand.

'Curse it!' he said. 'I can't hold it, I've no feeling in my hands.' He looked from one to the other, the steaming mug and his fist, cramped by cold, unable to seize it. The Abbé was on his knees, holding up his head, and made him drink it in sips while one of our party bent over his legs and untied the string round the newspapers.

By now all those who were not wearing gloves were beginning to feel their fingers tingling.

We put the man into a car, and the cavalcade went off in the direction of the Boulevard St. Germain, to look for an hotel with an empty room.

A group of people were clustered round the warm-air vent of the Underground. From the midst of four or five sleeping bodies emerged the torso of a kneeling man, head on one side, like one of those figures on the 1914–18 War Memorials. The Abbé Pierre reached across the sleeping forms and touched the man on the shoulder. The latter raised his grey-bearded, emaciated face, enveloped in a hood topped with a lump of snow. He looked at the priest with a disagreeable expression and spoke deliberately, in a deep bass voice.

'What do you want?'

'Don't stay there,' said the Abbé, 'go to an hotel.'

'Says you,' said the man after a pause.

Then, with a venomous dignity:

'You don't give a damn about us.'

'You're wrong,' said the Abbé. 'Here is some money.'

'Thanks,' said the man, putting out his hand.

The earth trembled as the rumble of a train passing beneath them increased, then died away. The frozen air seemed to melt in the hot wind which came up through the vent, and the heaped-up bodies were touched with a furtive wave of heat. Steam evaporated from the snow-sodden garments. Then the cold came back again, like a lump of crystal.

'Come on, Raymond,' cried Martel, and signed to his assistant to light up the group.

'We apologize for taking a photograph,' said the Abbé, 'but the journalists must do their job, so that the public will understand.'

'There's nothing to understand,' grumbled the man. 'F——the public.'

The sudden glare of the projector struck him in the face, and he shut his eyes, overcome; his long, hollow face suddenly took on the likeness of an old noble Gothic statue, worn by time. The pile of garments round him became alive, another face emerged, and fell back again.

It was once more dark. The Abbé put the question we all had on our minds.

'Why aren't you lying down like the others?'

'Bruises all over my body,' said the man.

Domino held out the mug of coffee and rum. The man drank it and said:

'Is it worth while waking the others?'

'Don't stay there,' said the Abbé, shaking an elbow, a head, here and there. 'Don't stay there. Go to a shelter. Here's some money.'

'Yes, Father,' came the muffled voices.

'Better to sleep like this tonight, and eat tomorrow,' said the kneeling man.

The arc-lights were out, and we could say nothing, for we were ashamed.

'Go to an hotel,' repeated the Abbé.

The man shrugged his shoulders and did not move.

Give them coffee, cheese, bread and money to go to the shelter of the hostel, whose red sign shone two hundred yards down the boulevard: what more could we do? Go away, knowing that they would keep the money to eat tomorrow, and that for the rest of the night they would stay and suffer on this vent of the Underground. But we stayed there, motionless and silent, miserable at our own helplessness. Impossible to avert these agonies. The terrible face of the kneeling man had closed up again, and only asked for peace, to be left alone. The Abbé leaned over them once more and, with a gesture, threw back his cape. His hand went out in adieu, or rather in benediction, and he murmured with an effort:

'Well . . . all right.'

Then he repeated: 'Good-bye.'

He could not say 'good night' to men who were to spend

such a bad night. That would have been an atrocious irony.

For a few moments longer, we continued to walk up and down in the snow, fascinated by that black lump of pain, which exercised an attraction for us which we could not resist. Then we heard Martel rewinding his camera and saying to his assistant in calm tones: 'I think the motor is turning more slowly. The oil is freezing.'

These words had a slightly soothing effect on us.

The little blonde student turned towards him with a lively expression of anger, but Martel, busy with his apparatus, took no notice of her. How could he know what was upsetting her? He was doing his job. He stood outside and beyond the suffering which he witnessed but did not take upon himself. He too felt cold, but not with *their* cold. He was not inside their skins, inside their desperate hearts. It was perhaps a good thing at that moment that the recorder of these events should be free of compassion, for thus he could continue the necessary work of bearing witness, holding his camera in a grip which did not tremble, in contrast to Domino who, unable to bear more, had given up trying to photograph the group.

Druel, beside me, lit a cigarette and murmured:

'I wish to God that I hadn't come tonight.'

Suddenly the deep harsh voice of the kneeling man was heard, calm and commanding, admitting no refusal.

'Give me a cigarette.'

As though obeying a master, obsequiously, Druel held out his packet of Balto cigarettes.

'Keep the packet.'

His gesture seemed to do him good, and he sighed with relief when the man said thank you.

Then the Abbé murmured: 'Come on, let's go,' and we fled to our cars.

The little student tried to open the door for the Abbé, but she was trembling too violently.

'It's . . . it's appalling,' she said.

The cars drove off, past these men who were abandoned to the night.

In the shadow of the City Hall, beneath the magnificent gilded lions which watch over the entrance, were huddled together two creatures of the night, both blind; the white stick belonging to one of them glowed in the shadow of the steps. It was so horrible to see suddenly, in the camera lights, the whites of the woman's eyes—she was smiling as she drank her coffee, murmuring: 'Thank you, sir'—that the Abbé rushed over to two policemen, standing twenty paces away in the angle of the building and watching us. He cried:

'You must send them to a shelter.'

We heard the reply.

'That's all very well, but there are so many of them that we can do nothing—the Depot is full.'

Martel and his assistant followed the Abbé and trained their cameras on the policemen. It would make a fine sequence— the agony of the helpless and the indifference of the authorities.

'I don't want to be filmed,' said one of the officers, removing himself out of range.

'You must do something,' said the Abbé in despair.

The officer asked: 'Are they alive?'

'Yes,' said the Abbé.

'Then we can do nothing. If they were dead, we could take them to the mortuary. All we can do is to leave them alone.'

Then the Abbé cried out: 'There is a dogs' home for stray dogs, but none for humans.'

But the two officers shrugged their shoulders, and went off with slow dignified steps.

The newspapers published these indignant words of the Abbé the following day, and as a result, the Chairman of the Municipal Council ordered the police to send the homeless away from the neighbourhood of the City Hall, so that they could die further off. But out of pity, and risking a reprimand, the police refused to obey.

Our next stop was the Place du Châtelet, in front of the big theatre, lit up now for a gala performance of ballet, for which 'all Paris' had taken tickets. On the pavement, in front of the big stores, beneath the smiling glances of the wax mannequins behind the plate-glass windows, dark groups of people huddled together on the heating vents, in the full glare of the light. Others, however, had sought obscurity and solitude, either from shame or from fear of the police. Just off the main streets, still full of life, with their luminous signs, and the cars passing to and fro, they were hiding in the turnings and alleyways of the old, dead sections of the city, between blocks of buildings, defiant and secret as fortresses.

They were hiding in narrow streets around the City Hall, the markets, the Banque de France, with its curving walls, floodlit, yet full of shadows. In porches, behind the buttresses shoring up ancient buildings, they were sheltering, and in one space, one wretched man, his dog squeezed up against him, had buried himself in a pile of old sacking and rags. All you could see emerging were the head of the man and the black muzzle of the dog, side by side.

Our headlights revealed, leaning against a door, a big fellow, standing up, with eyes closed, who danced as he slept. His body, agitated from head to foot by St. Vitus's dance, trembled and shook. His organic disorder would subside for a moment, but the cold excited his nerve centres anew, whereupon his head would begin to wag, after which the shaking would affect the thin shoulders, run down the arms to the gnarled hands, and down the lower limbs to the knees. Thus perhaps, by these unconscious puppet movements, his body defended itself against the cold. But he was more awful to look at than the others, who were lost in a coma-like slumber, because it seemed that he would never have any respite, and one reached the point of wishing him peace at any price, even the price of death.

When we lifted a military cloak, covering a group of three Algerians, clad in thin jackets, who were bunched up against the porch of St. Eustace's Church, we saw that they were not asleep. Their eyes were fixed on us like animals surprised in the dark, and their teeth, exposed by drawn-back, bleeding lips, shone in their grey faces.

Near the Place des Vosges, at the end of a barricaded street where the road was up, Martel discovered two men lying in the hollow of a drainage ditch. They had stolen the protective covering off the pipes, and lay there in the ditch, like bodies at the bottom of a charnel house.

There was also a man who walked and walked, aimlessly, all over the place, so as not to be trapped by the cold, which would kill him. We could hear the clatter of his heels on the asphalt in the silence of the boulevard, and caught glimpses of his bent silhouette, held for a moment in the reflection from the glass of a café window: this man who had the courage to go on walking, to carry his fatigue a little further. He had no money, but he had his pride. He would not beg, even for a modicum of warmth which cost nothing but a little shame. We so often encountered this vagabond's silhouette by day, as well as by night, that we ceased to notice it. Now, as we followed the Abbé round, we discovered it once more. The shadow became reality, a man like ourselves, who lived, felt and suffered. It was impossible any longer to pass by on the other side.

Thus all these vague shadows coalesced into dense lumps of pain, abandoned to the attack of the freezing night, which bit to the bone. We saw a young prostitute in a red coat, white beneath her make-up, leaning against a doorway, in a hopeless attitude, like an owl nailed to a barn door. Was it a lesson in morality that she needed at such a moment? And there was a young couple, locked in each other's arms. They had come from Bordeaux to find jobs in Paris, and had been sleeping out of doors for two months, bereft of everything, their only refuge their love for one another.

A sandwich-man was asleep on a bench, so worn out by futile marchings up and down, that we had to take him by the arms to get him on to his feet, and drag him, only half-conscious, into a hostel where we massaged his emaciated limbs.

The cafés were closing. It was now 1 a.m. The cold was getting worse. We too were exhausted, but the Abbé's passionate energy had inspired and sustained us, and led us further and further on our unhappy course, from street to street, from the market, that area full of filth and poverty, to the other bank of the river, the Place Maubert, that age-old centre of Parisian poverty.

We knew how ineffectual were these rescues of ours, and that other victims of the night were shivering their hearts out in obscure streets from which it was impossible to dislodge them. In cellars, in garages, in backyards, in empty houses, behind a factory fence, in fireless shacks, they were congregated. The help we gave was negligible, certainly, but it was worth giving, if for no other reason, for the fact that the things we saw made us cease to take for granted the value and security of our own lives. The little blonde student murmured from time to time: 'It's terrible!'

And Druel, in peevish tones, kept on repeating that he was 'bloody mad' at having come, that he would have given a million francs not to have seen what we had seen. This meant that he had lost his peace—it meant that one either had to give one's all or quickly forget, as quickly as possible; or else take part with all one's strength in the fight against social injustice, against the indifference of public authority, and against private selfishness, in order that this intolerable shame might cease, and that this running sore in the body of France might disappear.

We made our way along the quays under the bridges, into encampments of rags, paper, sacks, packing-cases, the homes of the professionals in poverty—tramps, male and female, lost in dreamless sleep, sleeping silently with a retarding of the vital function akin to the winter sleep of marmots, human beings near the level of animals, hairy and greasy, whose dirt constituted a protection against the cold. When, with great difficulty and some remorse, we dragged them from their sleep to offer them hot coffee, a human expression lighted up these bestial masks, a child-like look, full of innocence, fear, pain.

Several recognized the Abbé and murmured: 'Thank you, Father.'

And as he kept on apologizing for having to photograph them, they stammered out politely:

'Certainly, Father, carry on.'

Whereupon the cruel glare of the arc-light dragged from the shadows the haggard faces, and sometimes in front of Martel's camera a woman managed to smile, her teeth clenched with cold. We felt so ashamed, and would almost have preferred them to spit their hatred at us and chase us off with curses. At last the filming was finished, and it was dark once more, and with relief we climbed back up the slope leading down to the quay, to our cars, parked on the boulevard, asking ourselves if this were not all a nightmare and when it would end.

The Abbé Pierre was more exhausted mentally and physically than any of us, but pity and anger kept him going, till there came a moment when he too flinched from the impossible task.

A Negro was sitting on the steps of the staircase which leads down beneath the Pont de la Tournelle, wrapped in a carpet and wearing a cap. His head was between his knees, his hands in leather gloves gripped his ankles. When the Abbé woke him up, we were astonished to see his black face emerge. Seeing the priest, he at once tried to rise to his feet and to remove his cap, but his legs gave way and he fell back on to the steps. The Abbé took his arm and he apologized: 'Sorry, Father.'

He had woken up very quickly, and his yellow, intelligent eyes regarded us with dignity. As soon as he realized that we were not police, he smiled. The ends of his carpet were pinned together on his chest with a safety-pin; this strange garment did not appear ridiculous but, on the contrary, resembled a priestly vestment.

When the Abbé held out to him the mug, in which he had poured the last drop of now cold coffee, the Negro bowed his head and took off his glove, trying to control his shivering. His thin hand, veined like the roots of a tree, lifted the mug to the level of his eyes in a silent toast.

The arc-light and the camera did not wait for the Abbé to ask the Negro's permission before going into action. Nevertheless, he continued calmly drinking in the sudden glare. With his rug over his shoulders and his solemn gestures, he seemed for a moment no longer a homeless wretch, with neither hearth nor home, but a priest at the moment of the Elevation. Then, as if nothing had happened, he gave back the mug, smiled, and said slowly:

'I have been baptized, Father.' The Abbé was doubtless about to reply: 'That is neither here nor there.' But fascinated as we were by this noble vagabond of the black race, he said nothing. The Negro added: 'Yes—at Dakar, by Father C.'

'Yes,' murmured the Abbé.

The lights at last went out.

The man went on to say that he was not a down-and-out, that he worked in a rubber factory, and that he slept out in order to economize, so that he might send money home to Africa—he was proud to tell us that.

The Abbé gave him his last bank-note, so that he could sleep at an hotel.

'I can't take it, Father. I can easily stay outside for another few hours. It's three o'clock.' And when the Abbé insisted:

'My folks at home need the money more than I do. If you like, I will send it to them.'

'Just as you wish,' said the Abbé softly.

Then there was silence, as we were overwhelmed before the realization of how boundless are men's needs. Not only the man before us, not only the unfortunates all over Paris were in need, but people far away in Dakar and elsewhere, all over the five continents. All over the world men were collapsing, of cold here at home, of hunger over there, everywhere at grips with an unappeasable poverty, everywhere crying out for help.

I walked back to the cars with the Abbé. As he opened his door he gave way for a moment and hid his head in his sleeve, his elbow on the roof of the car. I put my hand on his shoulder, afraid he was going to faint. He was weeping. I could not understand this sudden flow of tears—the sight of this fine, courageous man had seemed far less terrible than the sight of those miserable numbed creatures, who had reverted to the condition of animals beneath their rags, for the priest was protected by his faith against despair. He muttered:

'He was baptized by Father C., whom I knew. I did not tell him I knew him.'

Then I half-understood what this groaning in spirit meant. We who baptize the African native, we who take charge of his soul, have therefore also accepted responsibility for his bodily welfare. And what have we done about it?

This Negro had renounced his primitive faith, his country, his climate; full of hope and affection he had entrusted himself to our Christian civilization, to our democracy. And God knows what he had suffered in Paris, friendless as he was—not merely physical privations, but also humiliations. But his soul had not been stained by his miseries, or by our selfishness and wickedness. But how many of his black brothers have not been corrupted by us, and become pimps, drug-traffickers, thieves, murderers?

'May God forgive us all,' muttered the Abbé, adding quietly, 'Time to go home.'

When Druel went up to him to shake hands, I recalled what he had said at the outset of the trip, that 'the priest made these tours for political purposes. Charity, the weapon of the political careerist.'

Now he had reached the hard kernel of truth. His mute look towards the priest was apologetic. This night marked for him, as for many of us, a turning-point in his life.

8

GRÉGOR'S MOTHER

ONE AFTERNOON at the end of January I met Antoine
in Paris. He was alone, sitting at a table in Robert's café,
near the market, dreaming into an empty glass. Over his
sailor's jersey he wore a beige raincoat, too light for the season,
and in spite of the cold he had opened the collar, revealing his long
neck. He was shivering. The skin, beneath reddish patches, was
livid, and his eyes were red, as if from weeping.

'Aren't you driving with Silvio today?' I asked him.

'No. The lorry has broken down. I've asked for the afternoon
off.'

He looked at me mistrustfully, frowning with his thick black
eyebrows. He lit a cigarette.

'What's gone wrong?' I asked.

'I'm thinking of leaving Emmaus. I want to find Grégor. He
was my pal. He's a hefty brute, but a good sort, and as simple as
a child. I believe he needs me. He's just a big kid. He was always
asking my advice about one thing and another. He used to say:
"I would like to become a regular guy, but I can't get around to
it. There's violence in my blood. What can I do about it?" I
did not know how to answer him, because I felt the same way as
he did. I told him that the main thing was to stick it out. Peaceful
conditions would come in time perhaps, and one would be able
to fall in with the crowd, and to be reconciled to oneself also.
He only felt at peace when he was singing in the dormitory, and
accompanying himself on the guitar. Everyone used to stop and

listen; they were fascinated. Now he's gone. I am afraid for him. I must find him. But it upsets me to leave Silvio and the boys.'

He was silent for a little, then he resumed: 'Sometimes Emmaus seems to me a pointless effort. We bring in the poor wretches who have been chucked out of everywhere else . . . while the foul world continues to grind down more of these hopeless types, and the more that arrive at Emmaus, the better everyone is pleased.'

'You know that's not the case.'

He began to tap the table with the stem of his glass.

'Yes, it is. I know all about it. We shan't get out of it that way. It's no good trying to reconcile fellows to life. It's no good trying to improve them. You must make them bad, till they don't mind going back and smashing everything, the banks, the churches, the fine houses, the Houses of Parliament.'

'Violence is the way out?'

'Yes, violence. That's what Grégor used to say. This army that we are by now at Emmaus—what if we were all to march on Paris! And it would be just too bad if some of us were beaten up by the cops.'

'The Abbé Pierre is neither a simpleton nor a fanatic.'

'He's a priest. He believes in God. He thinks God is good, that men can become good. I *don't* believe that God is good. One of my brothers was born an idiot. Luckily he died. And my mother has cancer, and will never get better.'

He was paler now and his hands were shaking. What could I say? So much unhappiness, and so young.

Out in the street, he seemed terribly upset. He said: 'Come with me to the Montagne Ste-Geneviève. I want to go and see someone.'

He was afraid of being alone. He attached himself to me as if I could help him, but I felt clumsy in the presence of his distress. I had known other boys like him, given to extremes, who in moments of despair at coming into contact with the cruelty of this world submit to the temptation to become terrorists. What use are words like patience, resignation, acceptance, to such as these? I tried to tell him he was wrong. Emmaus had not given in. We were fighting against injustice in another way, with different methods.

Suddenly he said in a far-off voice:

'I haven't seen the Abbé Pierre yet.'

His anger died away. He walked on, with his long ungainly stride, his head lowered.

'You mustn't let down the Abbé, and Silvio, and your pals.'

'I know. The best things about Emmaus are the friendships. But I don't think I am much use to them.'

'How many families have you brought in this week?'

'Anyone can do that. I can't think why I'm alive.'

'Just for that reason.'

'It's not enough. I want to do big things. It's not an achievement, to find homes for families.'

'Yes, it is,' I answered.

He only shook his head. Then he said: 'I don't care for anybody, and nobody likes me.'

'What about your mother?'

'Nobody really needs me any longer.'

When we reached the Montagne Ste-Geneviève, I told him I would wait for him in a café.

'No,' he said, 'come with me, I'm going to see Grégor's mother. Perhaps she knows where he is.'

We went on walking, while he talked in thoughtful tones: 'Grégor often used to say to me: "I must go back and do my bit with them. Then we'll go to the Riviera, you, my mother and I, and there we'll be free." When I used to ask him who these people were, he used to shut up. One day he mentioned something about "the fellows in the gang".'

'If his bit meant getting money from a theft, would you have thought that was all right?'

'No, no. But if he stole for his mother, I would not think badly of him. Perhaps he is with her now.'

.   .   .   .   .

The old lady was in bed, not because she was ill, but because she was cold. She had slipped under the eiderdown, fully clothed, a woollen shawl over her shoulders and a black scarf round her head, which made her look like an old peasant woman. She was spending the winter in the Russian fashion, in bed all day, hibernating indoors, behind closed windows and doors, for four months. When I pushed open the door of the dark room, I smelt the odours familiar to my childhood of the Ukrainian winter, the fug, the tea and biscuits, the anisette, the salted ham, and candlewax.

She had no electric light, and when we knocked she was resting in the dark, dreaming of her past, and of her sons, who had vanished one after the other. The heavy dusty curtains were drawn over the window, and the street lamps in the square twinkled through the holes in the material, which was nearly worn out. The candle which she lighted, and which stood beside the bedside table, flattered the little interior with its soft light, causing sparkling reflections to spring from the copper ikon, from several engravings on the wall, from the samovar bubbling on the stove. Multi-coloured embroideries and odds and ends of silk covered chest-of-drawers, table and chairs. The tiny flame, mercifully, did not reveal dirt and dust.

'So you are Grégor's friends?' murmured the old lady. 'I am glad. Thank you for coming. Wash three glasses, have some tea and pour me some, please. Oh, I am cold, cold as I have never been. How is Grégor?'

She looked so closely at Antoine that the boy turned to me with a wild look, imploring my help. She fixed him with her one good eye, confident and clear, and said in her fine, sing-song voice, which had remained young: 'What is going on? Tell me, young man, why have you got that disagreeable expression? What is upsetting you? Give me your hand.'

Antoine managed to conjure up a smile. He must have been thinking of his own mother, far away in the hospital at Brest. She smiled too, and asked:

'Is Grégor happy at Emmaus?'

'Yes, yes,' answered Antoine in a whisper.

'Tell him to keep calm, and not to drink, and not to fight. And he must not come to Paris. He still has two years' banishment to run, and he would be tempted to go and see that wretched woman again, and that gang of criminals who misled him. He is a decent enough boy at heart, but weak-willed. I was expecting him today. I can't think why. When you came upstairs, I thought it was he at last. Listen.'

She sat up in bed. Her face was tense as she turned in the direction of the door. On the wooden staircase, a heavy tread was mounting: the heavy, nailed boots of a tired man, counting each step painfully, as they creaked beneath his weight. Grégor's mother whispered:

'No. It isn't him.'

But her face still shone with hope, her look pierced the closed door, and seemed to cry out: 'Come in, come in.' The boots went on to a higher floor, and a door slammed.

Antoine had hoped too and, like her, had sat upright. Now his body slumped down with disappointment. She sighed, and asked us to draw back the curtains a little.

'Over there, opposite,' she said, 'lives a very old gentleman, alone. He used to be an accountant. I know him, but he does not know me. He only has his old-age pension to live on: £3 a month, that's all he has. But like me, he prefers the freedom of a tenement to the almshouse. Yes, he would rather steal the cat's meat from our neighbour's yard, which I did a fortnight ago. I hadn't eaten any meat for three weeks. We would rather have that than imprisonment and the disgrace of a home. Yesterday his skylight was not lighted, nor today. I must go round tomorrow and see if he is all right.'

She laughed all of a sudden.

'But things are going better with me. People are scared because of the cold, and they come to see me, to have their fortunes told in the cards. I've always been a bit of a clairvoyante. Yesterday a very wealthy client of mine, who thought the cold spell meant the end of the world, gave me £2.'

She gazed out of the window, then lay back on the pillow, shivering. I let the curtain fall, and it seemed as if the mysterious friend of the old lady, over there in his dark tenement, was inexorably abandoned.

'We haven't yet suffered enough in France,' she whispered. 'France has not yet reached the heart of suffering and fear. Now the great winter has come, like our Russian winters. Maybe there will not be a revolution, with spilt blood, and all the other atrocities committed in hatred. Because God loves France too well. But if He does, let him send enough tears for the rich to weep. I would have a cold spell so terrible, so prolonged, that the rich too would feel it in their bones. May their pipes burst, their gas and electricity be cut off, and their children cry in the night. May there be no coal for them, may their cars be unable to leave the garage to take them away to the Riviera to get warm. Oh, may God cease to be good to them, and become just and terrible. Then perhaps they'll begin to realize their kinship with the rest of humanity.

'If I don't get any more clients for the cards,' she continued, 'I shall sell my sewing-machine in the market at Mouffetard. The day before yesterday I went there. It was terrible. A foot away from the braziers, you were frozen. I wrapped myself in newspapers under my clothes and wore three pairs of stockings. But think of the poor people in these unheated barracks of buildings all over the place. Tell Grégor not to catch cold. Look and see if there is a light in the old gentleman's skylight.'

'No, it's still dark.'

She lay back, her eyes shut, muttering: 'Tell Grégor to be careful. Tell him I want to see him.'

9

THE TENT

AT THE intersection of two narrow streets, there was a piece of land, fifteen feet square, which was bordered on the pavement side by the remains of a wall and a wooden fence and trellis. High blank walls enclosed the other two sides. The locals had used this corner for a rubbish dump; they had thrown household remains over the fence. On the mounds of débris, nettles and wormwood were growing. Underneath the jam-tins, the rags and the lumps of snow, could still be seen the red tiles of a former kitchen floor. Holes gaped in the leprous soil. Steps disappeared into cellars, half-filled with garbage.

Antoine and I passed this wilderness earlier in the afternoon. Now, at dusk, an army-surplus three-poled tent of grey canvas had been erected there. Against a post, near a stretch of wall where a torn poster proclaimed: 'Film Society Meeting. *The Blood of a Poet*', hung a placard declaring 'Ragpicker Builders of Emmaus'.

When we got there the Abbé Pierre's car had already left for the rescue work, followed by the reporters' car. On the pavement, at the entrance to the tent, stood a large and lanky shape. By the light from nearby windows and the lamp-post I recognized Jérémie, the veteran of Indo-China, one of the first men of Emmaus. He had the head of a bandit, a curly beard, and his lower lip hung in a perpetual pout, revealing large, greedy teeth, usually gripping the stem of a short pipe.

On recognizing me, he raised his great arms, and in a deep bass voice he welcomed me, like a monarch at the gate of his palace.

Charles the Jockey raised the tent flap. They invited us in, and seated on straw they told us their story from the beginning. It was later completed by Jean-Pierre, and the others.

That very morning Jérémie had cut his hand (which was now bandaged) with a pruning-knife, and had come to Emmaus to have it seen to. At midday the Abbé Pierre, followed by Jean-Pierre, opened the door of the refectory and announced that an idea had come to him while he was saying Mass, namely, to plant, in the centre of Paris, on a piece of land which had been put at his disposal, a tent to shelter the homeless. He asked for volunteers. Jérémie had immediately come forward, and Charles and three newcomers. Jean-Pierre had taken them in a lorry to the site, where they had arranged to meet the man who was to sell them the tent. At the appointed time, the Abbé was there with the owner of the tent. With his bare hands he tried to undo the barbed-wire which attached the barrier to the wall.

'We need a pair of pliers,' he declared.

He seized one of the fence poles, and began to tug. The effort made the wings of his cape whirl in the air. They all set to and at last, with a groan, the planks gave way. The tent-owner's lorry backed in from a deserted street.

Jérémie let down the tailboard. The roll of hard canvas was nearly a yard wide and weighed at least half a ton. The Jewish seller, from whom the Abbé had bought most of the tents to shelter the families, the ragpickers and the factory workers, declared that he had never himself put up a tent of such dimensions.

'Let's start by getting it out,' said the Abbé. 'You'll find it has to be rolled on its supports like a cask.'

They did so, and when they let it go down the ramp, it rolled out on to the ground and came to rest on the spot chosen for it, as if it were already taking possession. There it was, unrolled like a carpet, the Abbé directing operations, showing where to put the pickets, and so on. The people of Emmaus busied themselves unfolding, with frostbitten fingers, the thick stuff, scaly like a snake's skin.

The old-stagers had erected many a tent before now, but the newcomers, in their anxiety to please the Abbé Pierre, went at it with too much enthusiasm and got caught up in the ropes and folds, trod on the canvas and could not find the holes through which the ends of the poles had to pass.

In his resonant voice, which echoed round the encircling walls, Jérémie shouted advice, which did not help at all, but he was happy. He had forgotten his bad hand, and imagined himself back in the good old days of the beginnings of Emmaus when, the numbers being fewer, he had worked side by side with the Abbé who since that date had often been taken away from Emmaus by other work, and of whom one now only caught glimpses in the distance.

That was why Jérémie was shouting so loud, to convince the Abbé that he could still count on him. The others were all doing the same thing. What roused the enthusiasm of both veterans and newcomers was that the undertaking was 'in the spirit of Emmaus', an improvised initiatory action, which vital necessity imperiously demanded; a defiance of both public and private passivity.

It was suddenly realized that no one had a hammer. The Abbé went to borrow one from a nearby café. With heavy blows on a spot between the tiles of the erstwhile kitchen, he hammered in the first picket. Underneath was limestone.

The lorry had turned at the corner of the Rue Laplace, and its headlights were trained on the work.

At the first blow the blinds flew up on the opposite side of the street, and from other windows the shapes of intrigued individuals could be seen looking out. The lights which sprang up inside the houses were an additional help to the workers. Some passers-by, including a party of students coming from the Place du Panthéon, stopped, and a joker asked if they were setting up a circus.

One of them recognized the Abbé and cried: 'It's the priest of

Emmaus.' One or two put down their brief-cases and came forward to give a hand. Two policemen coming down the street halted and watched the work for a few moments. Then one of them asked the Abbé:

'What are you up to?'

'I'm doing my job,' remarked the Abbé with a smile.

'Does the plot belong to you?'

'I've got the owner's authorization.'

'Have you got the documents? Come with me to the police station.'

Everyone had stopped working.

'I'll be back,' said the Abbé. 'Carry on without me. Jean-Pierre, telephone to a fodder merchant for the straw. I think there's one in the Saint-Antoine district.'

He went off with one of the policemen. The other stayed where he was on the street corner. Jérémie spat and swore. Jean-Pierre went to the café to telephone.

Three or four out-of-works had approached, and stood watching. They were the habitual wanderers of the district, whose footsteps guided them unerringly towards any free shelter. Bearded, filthy, with haversacks over their shoulders from which stuck out the neck of a bottle, hands in the pockets of their threadbare overcoats, and their scarves tied round their necks, they were all alike. With them was a North African and a young man wearing a windjacket. None of them offered to help.

Jérémie had hung up on the fence the placard hurriedly painted during the afternoon by Domino: 'Emmaus Ragpicker Builders. Neuilly-Plaisance.' At last, from among the group of spectators, a husky voice said slowly:

'Want a hand?'

'Yes,' said Jérémie, 'but leave your bottle, you'll break it.'

Meanwhile, the shapeless thing on the ground was beginning to come alive, to stretch, to rise up. A cone appeared, but fell back again on Charles the Humpback, who had slipped underneath to hold up the ridge-pole and who, indistinctly but forcibly, was swearing at this gang of freaks who couldn't co-ordinate their efforts. He was answered by raucous barks from Jérémie.

'The poles are not long enough,' cried Charles from beneath the canvas.

There was a moment of confusion. The late owner of the tent had departed. It was impossible to put up a tent which could not be kept upright. But it was suddenly perceived with relief that each pole was comprised of two staves which fitted into one another, and that one half had been left behind in the lorry.

The Abbé returned with the news that after a stiff beginning the police had relented and realized that the men of Emmaus were only doing what they themselves should have been doing, namely, sheltering the homeless, and had given permission for the tent to be erected.

The heavy covering, dragged up by twenty pairs of hands, began to flutter and spread itself, like the sail of a boat, till all at once the canvas cracked, stretched, went rigid, and the three-pronged tent took shape. A square opening faced the street.

The Abbé went inside, and shone a torch all round.

'We can get sixty people in here,' he said. 'Now we want straw, lamps, and stoves. Someone come with me, the rest can flatten down the earth. We must think of everything. We'll put the buckets at the bottom of the bit of ground.'

This last remark of the Abbé's fired Jérémie with enthusiasm.

'What a man! Thinks of everything, he does, even the bogs. . . . I'd never have thought of that.'

10

MEN ON THE STRAW

MIDNIGHT HAD sounded from the church of St. Etienne-du-Mont. Jérémie went to the café near by to fetch a cauldron of soup. For the third time Antoine whispered to me that he wanted to leave; but he did not move, continuing to sit there on the straw.

'What's the matter? Are you ill?' I asked him.

He groaned: 'I'm quitting.'

'Where to?'

'Don't know.'

His lower lip drew back in a snarl. His dust-covered face contracted, as though he were going to be sick. His whole body was trembling. I had been wrong to let him go drinking after we had left Grégor's mother. I had forgotten he once told me that he had a weak head for alcohol.

'Drink a bowl of soup, it will warm you up.'

'I'm not cold.'

He stared at the lorry-load of some forty poor wretches which Jean-Pierre and the Abbé had collected during their first tour of the evening. They were coming to life on the straw, drinking their bowls of soup, and stretching out their hands towards the four stoves standing along the centre of the tent. The air was thick with dust. The lamp hanging from the pole shone feebly upon their mask-like faces, and left the bottom of the tent in shadow, where the rolls of straw bedding were piled up. From this straw, from the coverings and garments wet with snow, and from those filthy bodies, rose an acrid smell which reminded one of army bivouacs. This smell, and the stable dust, the rustling of straw, the flapping of the canvas in the breeze which had sprung up, those tired voices and those shadows in the feeble light of the night lamp, all suggested the halt in the night of a regiment exhausted after a long route march. However, a troop of soldiers or a band of pilgrims marches towards a goal with hope, whereas these wanderers would resume their march next day with no other aim in view than to survive till nightfall. Their day would be spent in an exhausting tramp over the pavements, from one office to another, to Labour Exchanges, and from one soup kitchen to the next.

Numbed by fatigue as they were, they were all very quiet, and spoke little. The majority, after drinking their soup, rolled themselves in their coverings and were immediately asleep. One group continued to argue in low tones and almost confidentially with Jérémie and Charles.

While awaiting the Abbé's return, I had stretched myself out on the straw, and Antoine, shivering, whispered to me:

'I can't stay here.'

'What's the matter with you? You've drunk too much. It's not cold in here. Go to sleep.'

'No, I've not drunk too much. You don't understand. Listen to them.'

Wisps of straw hung from his shock of red hair. The dust discoloured his eyebrows and stuck to the sweat on his temples, round his nostrils, on his chin, tracing out the furrows and wrinkles in his skin and making him look old. His eyes were bloodshot.

'You don't understand. Listen to them.'

No, I did not understand why he was upset. I listened to the men at the other end of the tent. They were discussing something or other, calmly and amiably.

'I'm a sandwich-man,' said one, 'which is hard on the feet.'

'Keep your boots on, or we won't be able to breathe.'

No more was needed to make them laugh. And another was describing, without bitterness, as if it were a perfectly normal state of affairs, how, not having any permanent address, he could not draw his unemployment pay for six months, and how, if he *could* have done, he could have afforded to *have* a permanent address.

'When you've only got one shirt,' said the other, 'you can't wash it every other day; and a dirty collar, especially in my business, makes a bad impression when you go to be interviewed for a job. I was a pastry cook, and I've been out of work for a year.'

'I used to work in the Post Office, a night sorter on the railway post vans. In 1945 the train was bombed. They did not grant my disability, although ever since I have been unable to sleep at night. I was caught inside the post van, when it turned upside-down and caught fire. I only got out by a miracle.'

'I was a docker in Nantes. There's plenty of work for me there, and my family is there, but I have been banished for two years. There's nothing to be done about it. I've got no work, and my wife is starving.'

'I was two years in a sanatorium. I'm cured, and not infectious, but no one will employ me.'

'I travel in wines, but you have to pay for samples in advance, and if you haven't a fiver . . .'

'I was . . . I was . . .'

Among the sleepers was the Negro whom the Abbé had found near the Pont de la Tournelle, still in the same place, and a distributor of leaflets, who had sent his wife and children to relatives in the provinces, for he did not earn enough money even to rent an hotel bedroom.

One man, wearing a good overcoat, explained that he had been an accountant but that, at the age of forty-five, he was considered too old and could not find any opening. Some young agricultural labourers, who had come to Paris at the beginning of winter to try their luck, and some North Africans, had roamed the city for months, moving from one shelter to another and barely managing to keep alive.

They told their stories in calm tones without rancour, as if it concerned someone else, as if they were detached from their own destinies. Their resigned lassitude, their avowal of helplessness, revolted Antoine.

'Listen to them,' he said. 'It's not true that nothing can be done, it's not true! Why don't they kick up a fuss?'

I tried to explain that they had used up all their vital energy in the day-to-day struggle to keep alive. The worst ordeal, harder to endure than hunger, is to have to spend one's days alone in the midst of the crowd, and not to have anywhere to hide from the passers-by and the police. This solitude was what made them talk, and talk quietly, for it was no good dissipating the little strength they had left. They now had shelter, companionship, and people who bothered about them. After long days of silence, they could talk. And they hoped great things from us, they believed in the people of Emmaus. Moreover, the worst of their suffering, their shame, their fear, they kept to themselves, in the most secret recesses of their being, where they did not dare penetrate themselves.

Antoine did not understand this, because he was young and had within himself the urgent need to believe in a world where everyone would fit in, where each man would be able to solve his own particular problem. This world would be born one day, and he must not be deprived of the hope of it. I even told him he must do all he could to hasten its coming.

Among the refugees whom the Abbé Pierre had brought in were two couples. One woman looked old and fat. She came forward, bent, with uncertain steps. A silk scarf in loud colours was round her head. Her out-of-season coat was open, revealing a dress stretched tightly over her large stomach. A tall thin young man, about twenty-five, supported her, fussed around her, tenderly guiding her steps over the straw, between the sleeping forms. When she passed beneath the lamp, she raised her head, and we saw that she was not old and fat, but young and pregnant. She pulled her husband down to the bottom of the tent, to the darkest corner of it. She felt ashamed, and she was frightened, afraid of being separated from her husband, as had happened in the other shelters. It was in order to stay together that they had sat down in a corner of the quay where the Abbé had found them. Their names were Bernard and Jeannette. We had often run across them, and they were always on the move.

The other couple were the two blind old people whom the Abbé had found near the City Hall. He led them to an empty corner, and poured them some soup. They stammered their thanks. They were humble and apologized for taking up room on the straw. Reporters and photographers had now arrived and trained their cameras on the two trembling blind people. They did not know that their tattered clothes and scared faces were exposed to the flashlights and to the scrutiny of the reporters, and that thereby they became living proofs of neglect. The Abbé stood on one side, so that the photographers could snap them. It was not he who needed to be photographed, but these victims whom he had saved. He had given them warmth; it was for the journalists to give them light, the light of publicity. The flashes did not penetrate their dead retinas. The old woman grasped her bowl of soup with one hand and clung to her companion with the other; she was half in tears, half smiling.

When the Abbé went off again, with his escort of journalists, Antoine said to me: 'Let's go outside.'

'Is that all that life means?' he said to me when we got outside. He was in despair, losing his faith in Emmaus.

'Don't you think,' I said, 'that the Abbé himself has often echoed that cry?'

He pondered for a while, then said:

'Do you think I can really be of some use at Emmaus?'

'Of course. There aren't all that many of us.'
'That's true. Then I'll stay.'

That night the Abbé Pierre slept on the straw in the tent beside those he had rescued.

11

THE APPEAL

O N THE first of February I said good-bye to my friends in the Community at Neuilly. By midnight I should be on the Côte d'Azur.

The Abbé Pierre was away laying the foundations of the first Emergency City at Courbevoie. Domino and Jean-Pierre were with him.

At the bottom of the park, in the fog, Antoine was burning old papers, rags, and odds and ends not worth preserving. He was doing this with Dudule, one of those men whom the Abbé, with a kind of tenderness, called 'warped'. Gentle, slow, silent, he was a grown-up child to whom only the simplest jobs could be entrusted.

'So you're off?' said Antoine, leaving the bonfire and walking at my side down the avenue with its bare branches which traversed the deserted park.

'I'm going to say good-bye to Father Lucas,' I said. 'Come with me.'

A few days previously the priest had been brought back from Pontault, where he had fainted from fatigue while saying Mass. They had put him to bed at the Hermitage, in one of those monastic cells which the Companions of Emmaus had built at the bottom of the garden, not far from the Chapel. There, the men in charge and passing guests could stay and be apart from the life of the Community. There, too, those priests who formed the Brotherhood could make their retreats undisturbed.

The Abbé Lucas was lying with eyes closed on a camp-bed in his cell, which was heated by an electric radiator. His illness was not serious: fatigue and bronchitis, which would be cured with penicillin injections within a fortnight.

He was more than sixty years old. He had left the security of a monastery in the Sologne, of which he was the Superior, and renounced the contemplative life which suited his temperament, to share the life of the ragpickers of Emmaus. This mystic, with frail health, had not been equipped for that kind of battle. He had slept in tents, in vans, under the stars, tramped the roads of his strange parish of two hundred Companions and five hundred families in all weathers, and visited in turn all the workshops and centres with which the movement was concerned.

The fragile little man had baptized children and adults, celebrated marriages, and conducted funerals, but his functions did not end there. He had been compelled to intervene, on the human plane, to reconcile couples who had quarrelled, or to calm down drunken brutes. He had invariably respected people's freedom of conscience, and had received their trust and friendship in return. He had given himself to Emmaus, and Emmaus had made good use of him. He looked at Antoine and murmured:

'I've seen you before. What is your name?'

'Antoine. I used to work at Pontault.'

'Emmaus is becoming too big. We no longer know one another. It is growing too fast. We can't stop its growth. It's not merely that it is growing—it's changing its nature. Emmaus is entering the world. That's dangerous for us in two ways: too much glory, too much sickness and sorrow. This popularity will be the Abbé Pierre's cross. You must pray hard for him. We need so many men, young men like you, Antoine.'

What distressed Father Lucas was to have to leave the Community. He recalled all those who suffered from remorse, who were obsessed with hatred, who were disappointed in love, who were rebels, all those who needed the help which he felt he could give. The Abbé Pierre, always busy in Paris, had become inaccessible. The heads of workshops and the engineers were busy with the technical problems of the enterprise, and had no time to listen to confidences. Father Lucas had been lawyer, psychiatrist, counsellor, as well as confessor and attentive friend to these sad solitaries, wounded by life, and now convalescing. We left him, a thin white hand raised in blessing and farewell.

Back in the refectory, Alfred had turned on the ancient radio as he did every day at noon. The lads listened to its wheezing and continued to chatter and drink their soup. Alfred liked to hear the news. He leaned over the radio, shaking his great red head, surmounted by a cap of doubtful whiteness, while his henchmen served in the dining-room. He raised his voice to comment on the weather announcements.

'Listen—12 degrees at Poitiers last night, below zero at Luxeuil. It'll freeze again.'

On this particular day he had scarcely tuned in when the speaker announced: 'A message from the Abbé Pierre.' Alfred began to yell: 'Shut up, you fellows. Father's going to speak.'

The noise subsided as the well-known voice came through, speaking urgently, in anguished tones.

'We need your help, my friends . . .'

The silence was complete. All the men had raised their heads, and turned towards the radio as if the voice had summoned each of them by name.

'We need your help, my friends. A woman has just died, frozen to death, at three o'clcok this morning, on the pavement of the Boulevard Sebastien. Every night there are more than two thousand souls lying frozen in the streets, without a roof and without food. More than one is virtually naked. In face of such horrors, the Emergency Cities are more than ever necessary . . .'

There were about twenty of us in the refectory, from the upkeep and cleaning sections, the office and garage staff, plus two newcomers. The latter sat looking down at their plates, unable to eat. The rest, who had been members of the Community for some time, only very seldom nowadays saw the Abbé enter this refectory. In the old days he used to come and eat with them every day, and talk to them on Sundays about the progress of the Community. Now it was as if he had come back from a long way off and was talking to them once more, personally. And at the same time he was talking to the whole of France, and this made them proud of their Father, their voice.

'By tonight, in all the towns of France and in each district of Paris, placards must be hung up beneath a lamp in the night, near all places where there are coverings, straw, soup, and they must bear the title *Rescue Centre* and these simple words: "You who are suffering, whoever you may be, enter, sleep, eat, take hope, for here you are loved."'

The twenty men who listened with closed eyes had once been of those wanderers of whom the Abbé Pierre was speaking, and had had the good fortune to find Emmaus, and food, work and friendship. They counted themselves among the privileged, and they could not listen to this appeal without wanting to do something, to give something to their brothers in Paris, to go there at once.

'I implore you, let us love one another enough to finish this business at once. May so much misery be the means of restoring to us that marvellous thing, the soul of France. Thank you, thank you, you can all help the homeless.'

Old Luke got up, took off his cap, and passed it round the tables. Some gave money, and those who had none gave cigarettes.

'We also need hundreds of volunteers, to ensure transport every night to pick up the homeless, and as supervisors at the Rescue Centres.'

Antoine gave his last three cigarettes, then looked at me in a dazed way, unable to hold his spoon, to stay in his place.

'Come on, I'm off,' he said. 'And this time for good, and as for you, you're not going to the South of France.'

'You're quite right—I'm not!' I said.

12

THE REVOLT

W HAT A damned commotion,' said Jérémie to me,
with a worried expression. 'What's got into them?
We were all so quiet here—and now . . .'
There was no room in the tent for the parcels of clothing and
blankets which, since the Monday afternoon, had not ceased to
pour in. What was happening? Why this sudden access of
generosity?

For three days, life in the tent had gone on calmly, following a
ruling of the Abbé Pierre and Jean-Pierre: the morning to be
spent cleaning out after the departure of the guests. A car belonging to the Public Health Department came to disinfect, and
released clouds of D.D.T. which penetrated the straw and the
coverings and killed the bugs. Monsieur Edouard, a retired business man, who had proffered his services on the second day, had
gone out shopping for the midday meal. Jérémie and some others
were busy clearing out the cellars, with the aid of some imple-
ments borrowed from the neighbouring café: in buckets and
laundry bowls they brought to light a mass of débris. In the first
of the cellars they had set up a kitchen. They had often received
gifts in kind, and food which had been shared out, but never as
on this afternoon of the 1st February had the parcels accumulated
like this, brought by a crowd of people, who seemed at last to
have discovered the existence of the tent and realized what it
stood for. Never had so many inquisitive people been seen around

nor so many friends and volunteers. What contagion of goodness had suddenly attacked them all? Jérémie did not understand, because he had not heard the Abbé's appeal on the wireless. He did not know that the tent would become that very night the meeting-place of a whole people.

Since midday, in Paris and in the whole of France, hundreds of thousands of hands were emptying cupboards, opening dusty trunks in attics, tying up parcels, packing linen, food and cooking utensils. All this would converge on the two focal points selected by the Abbé: the Hotel Rochester and the tent on the Butte Ste-Geneviève.

This tidal wave of parcels, unloaded from lorries and cars, brought in pushcarts and on bicycles, had begun in the early afternoon to arrive at the hotel, to the consternation of the staff and guests. The offerings submerged the hall, the sitting-rooms, and even the cellars of the establishment. The wave, which had originated in the wealthy districts, now flowed towards the poorer districts, assaulted the Butte and threatened to block the entrance to the tent.

'What on earth has got into them?' exclaimed Jérémie, chewing his cigarette-end and trying to understand the phenomenon. As the afternoon wore on the movement accelerated. Lorries arrived from the City Hall with tons of bedclothes.

'There's no more room in the tent, Monsieur Jérémie,' repeated Monsieur Edouard, in a tone both confidential and alarmed, charged with unuttered implications, which was his customary way of speaking. The simplest circumstances invariably perplexed him.

'Fling them down there,' said Jérémie, shrugging his powerful shoulders, and indicating by a turn of the head the space between the tent and the walls of the neighbouring houses.

Some good-hearted students who were helping, seized a pram loaded with plates and saucepans, and carried it to the enclosure, where it was joined by a commode. A parcel of linen and a roll of carpet took their place on the pyramid, which grew rapidly by the continual depositing of clothing, utensils, furniture, shoes, packets of every shape and size, old and new.

'For the Abbé Pierre, for the Abbé Pierre!'

Jérémie stood motionless against the pole bearing the inscription, 'Ragpicker Builders of Emmaus', hands in pockets, indicating the pile with a nod of his head. He said no word of thanks. He had done the dirty work when Emmaus started. He had dragged old jampots and bottles out of the frozen mud for months on end, and only the previous night he had been hacking with his pick at the foundations of the future Centre of Refuge at Plessis-Trévise. Now he could keep his hands warm in the pockets of his ancient overcoat: of their own accord the objects were coming to him, the Man of Emmaus. The crowd were spreading offerings at his feet. For years Paris had ignored the grief and courage of men, but at last she had discovered and understood the sign of Emmaus. It was the day of revenge, and also of reconciliation, after so many years of crying in the wilderness.

'Day of Victory. A victory without shame, or fears, or remorse. Now a new era is beginning, when the long misunderstanding between rich and poor, the haves and the have-nots, will be cleared up.'

But he was worried as well as jubilant.

'What if this avalanche goes on . . .' And on top of it all, the 'guests' of the previous night returned to the overloaded tent, plus newcomers, scared and bewildered, who had been smoked out of their retreats by rescuers, as happy and proud of their exploits as hunters bringing home game.

Night fell, and the frost stung people's faces but did not induce them to leave. Windows all around were lit up. Charles and the students took out the stoves to light them on the pavement, an operation which would have been dangerous inside the tent because of the straw. The lamp-post in front of the École Polytechnique beamed down upon the scene. The crowd watched with friendly curiosity, as if they were being initiated into some obscure tribal rites. They glanced inside the tent, pityingly but eagerly, to see the rescued rolled in their bedclothes on the straw. A car brought soup from the Hotel Rochester.

I asked Jérémie if he had seen Antoine, who had disappeared immediately after lunch.

'No,' said Jérémie, 'I don't feel he'll stay long at Emmaus. He's too worried about his own little affairs. As if there were time for *us* to have any problems!'

At 9 p.m. Charles disconnected the lamps from the battery, and left only a nightlight on the entrance pole. The refugees, rolled in their bedclothes, slept in the warmth of the stoves. But outside, pedestrians, private cars, and civil and army lorries continued to discharge parcels of clothing, bedclothes, mattresses, kitchen utensils, stoves and more refugees. Meanwhile, those in charge of the tent tried to bring order out of chaos, to stack the parcels, and to arrange the gifts in heaps on the ground surrounding the tent. Despite the great cold, the workers had taken off their coats and were struggling quite out of breath against this tidal wave. Things were blocking the opening, and soon it would be impossible to walk on the ground for the mounting barricade.

Falling over the pile in the dark, getting their feet caught in the ropes, they passed the parcels from hand to hand, to the space in the angle formed by the two walls of the empty house. They tore the skin of their hands on sharp bits of metal, wood or china. Some pairs of shoes and boxes thrown over the wall could wait.

Then they beat a retreat. There were not enough of them to discipline the happy impetuosity of this invasion. The Abbé Pierre had played the part of the Sorcerer's Apprentice. His midday appeal on the radio had unleashed a force, the scope of which could not be assessed, a new and unknown force, unknown because rarely called upon, a people's generosity.

With their cargoes of charity and of curiosity, from the most distant areas of Paris, from Boulogne, Passy and Monceau, the smart cars, lost for the first time in this poor quarter, wandered around the byways of the Butte, coming up against first the crowd

and then the police, and finally stopping on the edge of the area
at the Place du Panthéon, or beside the École Polytechnique. The
bundles from the rich, passed from hand to hand above the heads
of the crowd, joined those of the poor on the pavements and in
the road. A depot was formed before the green shutters of the
Chinese restaurant at the top of the road. Troops of boy scouts
suddenly appeared and made a lane for received gifts, depositing
them in orderly fashion, preventing thefts. But on this amazing
night the very idea of theft seemed absurd: all this accumulated
surplus was for whoever lacked what was necessary, and the
poorest would come tomorrow to help themselves.

Beautiful young women in fur coats opened the doors of their
handsome cars, from which they produced tramps in rags, quite
bewildered, who had been picked up almost forcibly along the
quays ('I came just to please these ladies and gentlemen,' declared
one of them). But the tent was full, and as Charles the Jockey
observed: 'You can't put them one on top of the other.' So some
had to be taken to the police station, in the Place du Panthéon.
The Curé of Bezons, who had arrived in a lorry with a party of
young men, took a whole consignment of them to his remote
suburb. Cars began to act as ferries between the tent and the new
shelters which were being opened throughout the capital, in
underground stations, town halls, banqueting halls. Even at the
Mutualité Insurance Company's premises two hundred persons
were lodged on straw, given by the Republican Guard from their
barracks.

A movie van, with a camera on the roof, slowly made its way
through the crowd, followed by a television van. They stopped
against the fence. Technicians began to unroll wires and place
microphones at the entrance to the tent near the angle in the wall,
where the guy ropes were fixed. There the Abbé Pierre would
appear and speak. A projector lit up on the roof of the van, its
beams passing over the patient crowd which was waiting, silent
and half-stupefied, for the priest's arrival. The expressions on the

faces of the crowd, caught in the light of the projector, white and rigid with cold, showed a desire for action, a determined expectation, presaging the birth of a new order, of true justice and brotherly love. One had to realize that these men and women, young and old, of all sorts and conditions of life, brought that night to the Butte, not only curiosity or superficial interest, but also faith, together with bitterness and anger: the result of their need to believe in love once more and in their country, which had let them down.

Among that mass of people I recognized Marc and his friend, the big fair-haired fellow, and the Indo-Chinese. Their eyes were shining.

The projector was turned off at 10.30 p.m. In half an hour the Abbé Pierre would arrive.

A large hand was laid on my arm—Jérémie had left his post. He was fed up with all this commotion and wanted a drink. We made our way through the crowd and down the street to a quiet little pub, where he drank a pint in one gulp, and ordered another.

His throat was burning with D.D.T. dust from the straw, from the blankets, from the dryness of the air, and from the cigarettes he had smoked. This big fellow from the North of France only drank beer and occasionally Calvados. He distrusted wine. He had drunk too much in the army.

He raised his glass to drink the Abbé's health, the health of Emmaus, to his comrades there, to this great night, and to the favourable future in which he had not been deceived. Two years previously the ex-hero from Indo-China had been committed to a disciplined life to which he was incapable of adapting himself. Lonely, without money, ready to become a gangster, he had fetched up at Emmaus, where a new destiny, another kind of adventure, had thereupon begun. The Abbé Pierre trusted him and had chosen him to be responsible for the tent. Tonight was his apotheosis.

'Look at this.' His huge hand pulled from his pocket a heap of hundred- and thousand-franc notes. His hooded eyes were laughing, his big, dirty fingers closed over the money as if it were a fistful of bullets, a pocketful of dynamite; this was the weapon by which Emmaus triumphed.

He would take his wages, four hundred francs a week, but the rest was for the Abbé Pierre, on whose behalf he would at any time empty his pockets. Others were to rob Emmaus, but not Jérémie. He would keep nothing for himself, for if he did so, even a single note, he would lose in exchange one of the few things he still valued, his self-respect, the Abbé's confidence, the ability to look the world in the face. I don't believe he was ever even tempted.

He put away the money and said: 'So your friend Antoine has not come with you?'

'No. Do you need him?'

'No. There's something wrong with that boy. A week after his arrival at Pontault, they brought him back from the workshop. He'd fallen down, as if he were dead. He was dead, dead tired. He's a proud, restless type.'

He relighted the stub of his cigarette and murmured: 'Bloody little nuisance—Antoine,' but he said it with a sort of worried tenderness.

The café door opened at this moment, and I beheld a little man who always seemed scared. Ernest was one of my war-time pals. He had a white face, flabby and ugly, and very clear eyes behind strong spectacles. He gesticulated clumsily with hands which had never been able to hold a gun, and which were always afraid that people would not shake them in friendship. He had been a pain in the neck to our Radio Company during the phoney war in 1940. In fifteen years he had not changed in appearance, but the ridiculous person of former days seemed transformed, perhaps by the strange climate of this night, which lit a reckless light in his eyes and caused him to hold his bald head high.

ILLUSTRATIONS

Family life in a converted carriage
(Photos MATCH)

'Men on the Straw'

Installed at last in a 'real' home
(Photos MATCH)

More power to Emmaus from the refuse dumps
(Photos MATCH)

Cité de la Pépinière, Pontault-Combault (near Paris)
(Photo Roland BONNET)

The Abbé pays a call at Pomponnette
(Photos MATCH)

The avalanche of a people's generosity
(Photo Roland BONNET)

The Abbé working with his ragpickers
(Photos MATCH)

He recognized me, came to our table, and spoke to Jérémie.

'Are you one of the Emmaus boys?'

'Yes,' growled Jérémie.

'Shake hands.'

With a bad grace, Jérémie extracted his huge dirty paw from his pocket, and the other seized it in his small fists.

'What will you drink?'

'Beer,' growled Jérémie.

I noticed some marks like flour on Ernest's coat.

'What are you doing now?' I asked him.

'I have rented a cart, and I collect bread from all the bakeries, and bring it to the Rochester for distribution among the refugees.'

'I meant, your job?'

'In an office—to do with stationery.'

But it was obvious that it had little importance for him.

'The essential thing is to understand, isn't it?'

'What?'

'What is happening tonight.'

His clear, grey eyes fixed me with insistence, as if his look could transmit his thoughts better than words. He added: 'It's a new life that is beginning, you understand. I must talk to you about it. Here's my address.'

At the next table two gentlemen in fine overcoats had just sat down, and one said: 'Tell me, my dear fellow, what is going on? This priest, what is it he wants exactly? What does the Ministry say about it all? It is impossible to believe that all this shindy is simply over warming up a few tramps.'

'I'm just an observer,' said the other prudently. 'It's no use compromising oneself. But my wife insisted on going round picking up the homeless, and do you know what was our first contact with these people? We found a man sleeping on the pavement near the market. My wife got out of the car, woke him up, and told him to come to the shelter, and the fellow answered: "Go to hell, you're a bloody nuisance. This is the third time I've been woken up." The extraordinary thing is that my wife was not discouraged, but went off to look for more. I'm waiting for her here. What time is it?'

'Nearly eleven o'clock. The Abbé won't be long now. I'm curious to see him, and find out just what it is he wants. He is an intelligent man. He was once a Member of Parliament, and I bet he's ambitious. But he'll have to be very careful. He goes about too much, and he may not be able to stop himself in time. He's disliked in high places, that I know.'

The other lowered his voice.

'Do you know what a friend of mine, high up in the Ministry, told me yesterday? That the Abbé had better stick to his rag-pickers and his good works. If he goes beyond that, there are ways and means of keeping him quiet.'

The door opened and brought in a flood of cold and noise.

'It's a riot,' said one of the gentlemen.

Ernest got up nervously.

'He should be here by now.'

He was. He was standing in the angle of the wall, near the tent, a small figure in a black cape, surrounded by film cameras, projectors, and an enthusiastic crowd.

What did he say to these people, ready for violence, whom he could easily lead into battle? One thing the man at the Ministry had forgotten: he was a priest, not a demagogue. His enemies were waiting for words of violence, for a suggestion to the crowd which would have compromised his work for ever, and given the opportunity to send in the police, who up till now had remained passive and had even helped in this crusade. But the Abbé only said that they would find out later who was responsible for this state of affairs. The job right now was to save men in danger of death. Public authority had helped. Town halls and underground stations had opened to shelter these unfortunates. Big firms had put offices, lorries and goods at the Abbé's disposal. All over Paris rescue centres were being set up. But all this was only a temporary solution. The Government, pushed by public opinion, had decided to build emergency cities, and to inaugurate a campaign against the appalling conditions of living of a large proportion of the population. The man at the Ministry must have been disappointed.

13

THE END OF THE NIGHT

THAT SAME night at 3 a.m. in the cold little kitchen of the Curé of N., a working-class parish in the suburbs, the priest was able to declare in his peasant's voice as he lit his pipe: 'At last they're all under cover. But there's one thing I don't understand.'

'You'll understand in due course,' answered Domino, who had known him since they were both children. 'Come on, get out the bottle and give us a drink. My pal is shivering.'

My chest was burning, but the rest of my body was frozen to the marrow. The vibration of the lorry, during all these excursions, had got into my limbs. Domino's heavy arm fell round my shoulders. He was sweating, enclosed in his cushions of fat.

'You're going to the rot, my poor friend, with that cough. You'd better get back to the South of France, quick. What are you trying to find in Paris? Heartbreak?'

Yes, it was time for me to go. I would leave Paris in the morning, by the first train, and take with me not only heartbreak but something else as well, for which it was worth while risking one's health: a knowledge of the world greater than I had ever had, which I had to think over and define during my retreat. So, in spite of the fever and the physical pain which burnt in my lungs, I felt happy.

'I do not understand,' went on the curé pensively, pouring out some brandy, 'how I have been content to waste my time all these years and still feel pleased with myself. What have I done all these years, and thought I did well, in this working-class parish? Preaching, catechism, study circles. What is left of my conquest of souls in the end? How few people I have really touched. Usually those who needed it least. And all that time people were dying of hunger and cold, and I never noticed them. I have been too easygoing. I have been an accomplice of the Pharisees. I have been a Pharisee myself.'

The curé, a former soldier, examined his conscience honestly in our presence, puffing at his pipe as he did so. The two young Communist workers, who had been driving the rescue lorry, listened to him in silence, their faces contracted with surprise and with a kind of embarrassment, for the curé was so sincere that it made them feel awkward.

Our twenty-three rescued persons, among them two women and three children, were asleep on the straw in the adjacent church. The benches had been removed and the big stove, which was normally only used to heat the parishioners at the Sunday Masses, had been lighted. Never perhaps had those people sleeping on the straw been inside a church before—there were North Africans, green with cold, porters from the market, a group of tramps with a girl of twenty, beautiful, wild and filthy, a working couple with three children, and that strange pair of vagabonds, Bernard and Jeannette, whom the Abbé had welcomed to the tent on the first night and who had not come back. The curé had picked them up on the quays with a lorry lent by a factory and driven by the two Communists.

The curé was pouring out coffee and talking of Chartres. I heard him from afar off, as in a dream. He was saying how he had learnt that the flagstoned floor of the cathedral sloped down. The builders had taken into account that, following the law of sanctuary, many unfortunates would come there at night to sleep on the straw. In the morning they used to wash the steps, and the water escaped by the gutters. Then the doors of the Cathedral were shut. Nowadays the doors of every church were shut against the physical suffering of men, for the right of asylum had disappeared.

'I know,' the curé went on, 'why all I have done has been sterile, more or less: because I didn't begin at the beginning. The first move should be in the direction of physical health. Witness the parable of the Samaritan. Three weeks ago, crossing Paris by car with another priest, we saw a man lying in the street. Both of us behaved as if we hadn't seen him. The Abbé Pierre would have stopped. That's the whole difference.

'One of those poor creatures said to me tonight,' pursued the curé: ' "I have never shaken hands with a priest." Why? Perhaps none of us had ever asked him to. I've been living in another world, a world of words.'

Banging the table with his fist, he cried in sudden anger:

'I shall kick them out of my church, these refugees, if they come to Mass next Sunday just out of gratitude. They owe me nothing. First let them become men capable of reasoning. Then it will be time enough to discuss what to do with their reasoning powers.'

We went out into the courtyard. The moon was shining in a clear sky. Its rays glinted on the big stained-glass windows of the shadowy church.

The curé accompanied us to the gate, where the lorry of the two Communists was parked together with Domino's motor-scooter, on which I was returning to Paris.

Suddenly he stopped, and muttered as if to himself: 'I'm going to bed.'

'Well, good night,' said Domino.

'I'm going to a warm bed and that pregnant woman has to sleep on the straw. Come and help me carry them indoors, her and her husband.'

'You'll kill us,' said Domino, following him towards the church.

'The worst of it is,' said the curé, clinging to the heavy door of the church, 'that this idea of mine is so belated. And that it smacks of a heroic action, giving up my bed. Oh, what poor types we are, after our twenty centuries of Christianity.'

PART TWO

SPRING GROWTH

THE MISUNDERSTANDING

IN THE entrance hall of the Hotel Rochester a little old lady was having an acrimonious discussion with the porter. She held her parcel, wrapped in paper and carefully tied with red curtain-cord, in both hands.

Her black coif, like a lace tiara, placed on the back of her white hair, framed her pink wrinkled face. In her small suspicious peasant's eyes burnt the fixed idea which for days and nights had invaded all her small mental horizon.

'I want to give this to the Abbé Pierre himself.'

Her generosity, inspired by fanatical devotion, would have sent her to the world's end in search of the Abbé, so as to be able to give him personally this rug of multi-coloured wool which she had knitted for him, and for which she hoped to hear his 'Thank you'.

'Gifts are to go to the basement,' said the porter.

'Is the Abbé there?' Her little eyes shone.

'Of course not,' said the exasperated porter. 'He has other things to do.'

But she did not move. She tapped the parcel with her small pink hand.

'I wish to give it to him personally.'

'I tell you, he's not here.'

'Where is he?'

I went up to her and told her that he said Mass every day at St. Philippe du Roule, but that I did not know at what time—perhaps she could see him there.

'Is it far?'

'No. Come with me.'

But she still did not move. She was still suspicious, and doubt-less thought that I wanted to lure her outside to get rid of her.

I then asked her to entrust the rug to me, assuring her that I would give it into the Abbé's own hands as soon as he could receive me. But her fingers closed more tightly over the precious parcel, as if I were trying to take it from her by force. The blood left her face. Confusion showed in her eyes. She felt herself sur-rounded by enemies.

Around us, visitors, donors, voluntary employees, came and went, running to and fro and up and down stairs enthusiastically. And in the jostling crowd of busy, happy young people, the stubborn little old woman, clutching her parcel, was like a black stone in the midst of running water.

For the last ten days, in this same Hotel Rochester, hundreds and thousands of parcels like hers had accumulated in a gigantic pile which filled the basement, or else had been distributed. But the old woman doubtless thought that she was the only one to bring an offering from her village in the Beauce. For the Abbé's sake, she had undertaken this complicated journey. I felt sorry for her and thought that when I spoke to the Abbé Pierre the next morning, I could perhaps arrange a brief interview. In the urgency and number of arid tasks, isolated in his office with the organizers and the Centre leaders, or else with financial or political bigwigs, he had no time left for human contacts.

A man had come from Reims on foot to give him personally one thousand five hundred francs, his savings, and had apologized for having had to use a hundred and fifty francs of it for a snack. A child had emptied the contents of her money-box—for three years she had been saving to buy a bicycle and had collected ten thousand francs. A father had brought what he held most sacred, the boots which had belonged to his son who was killed in the war. An 'artist' from Toulouse had sketched in woollen threads a portrait of the Abbé, and he also had begged for an interview.

But in the hall, on the staircases, in the corridors of the big building, the mobile platoons, the secretaries, the collaborators of the Abbé Pierre had fulfilled their painful duty—they had protected him against that invasion of affection. These precious gifts had joined the enormous collection of anonymous gifts in the cellars, and their donors had returned to the provinces heartbroken at not having seen the Abbé Pierre—unless they had been capable of overcoming their distress in a spirit of sacrifice by remembering that their gift would go to its correct destination, to those poor people whose mouthpiece the Abbé Pierre was. If a tally of these generous acts is kept, it can only be by God alone.

'Is it far, this church?' asked the little old woman.

'Only five minutes away.'

We passed through the doorway into the twilit street where under a fine rain a procession of poor people waited their turn to give their particulars to the Rescue Office.

'Who are these people?' asked the little old lady, in disdainful tones.

I told her of the cases of distress which the Abbé Pierre tried to put right. We passed by the long file of young and old, of unfortunates, the weak-headed, the jobless, young girls and exhausted mothers of families, gazing into the windows of the luxury shops, which reflected their faces, ugly or dignified, insignificant or striking, but all bearing the marks of misery. They watched us pass in silence. One woman held a child by the hand. Most of these unhappy people had not come there to beg for the derisory benefit of a blanket or a pair of shoes: they hoped for real salvation from their condition, for the solution of a wellnigh insoluble social problem; for work and, above all, for a place in which to live, a status as human beings, a little justice.

I felt that her rug must weigh very heavily on the arm of the little old lady, so I said:

'Give it to one of these people, to that young woman, for example, with the little girl. I'm sure she would find it useful.'

She stopped abruptly, her eyes grew round, her mouth opened as if she were gasping for breath: 'What!' she cried. 'Give them the Abbé's rug? To people like that? It's for him I've made it, so that he can use it at night—not for people like that.'

And I felt the anger mounting within me in the face of this idolatrous and selfish love, which the Abbé Pierre himself would have disapproved of. The old lady did not understand, and so many others, young and old, did not understand what was the real object of their generosity. The whole of our movement seemed to be threatened by this misunderstanding, and all France to resemble this old woman. There would come a day when the Abbé Pierre would be silent, and then what would happen to his poor people? Who would take charge of them? Who would defend their cause? One should love the Abbé enough to identify oneself with him, and share his passion, but not on the basis of any human relationship with him. One must not yield to idolatry. The myth was a screen to hide the real problem. For if the immense fervour which, despite himself, he had aroused was not transformed in the people's hearts into love for all men, then everything remained incomplete and fragile, destined for quick oblivion, like any other human experiment.

2

STRIKE WHILE THE IRON IS HOT

T HE ABBÉ PIERRE was very clear in his mind that this
wave of popularity, which had come too quickly, would
recede equally quickly. The public does not become
enthusiastic about the same person twice. Therefore the undertaking must be insured against the dangers of this falling away; it must
be given security, and the seeds must be planted which could ripen
later. He wished to keep his hands free for this essential task. That
was why he could not welcome and thank all the little old ladies
who insisted on seeing him in order to give him a rug. He had to
conceal himself when leaving the hotel, when moving about the
streets. He used to say: 'I feel badly about this, but I must. My
time is not my own.' He travelled a great deal, having undertaken
lecture tours in the suburbs and in the provinces, where the
number of committees multiplied.

In the twilight, permeated with that odour of fires burning on a
wet evening at the end of winter, the torpid towns woke up, and
the population converged on the lighted peristyle of the Winter
Garden. The crowd spread over the steps and under the trees in
the square to hear him say: 'The poor are in our midst.' Then the
Prefect, the Mayor, the Red Cross ladies, with the support of the
parish priest, would organize galas and set up committees.

'The poor are in our midst! In our little town, so pleased with
itself in its tranquil hypocrisy, working men are sleeping six in a
room, in freezing blockhouses, in tents in the woods, while solitary old maids occupy flats with nine empty rooms. Self-employed

working girls do their work in hovels, old men die in icy attics. Statistics for all this have been mouldering for years in pigeon-holes in the Town Hall or the Prefecture . . .'

And he went from town to town, to keep alive this revolt, this will to make things better. Tottering with exhaustion on the plat-form, his eyes red from the glare of the lights, he spoke, saying that France had hitherto been like a corpse.

'Is France a dead body? No—she is stirring with life, but she has no soul. Yet because a few good-for-nothings said "no" to death, and said "yes" to love, the soul of France is reviving.'

He spoke of going a step further than the immediate rescue of the homeless: to the building of a just world.

On the other side of the footlights, hundreds of serious, atten-tive men and women had their eyes fixed on the speaker. They had not come to hear a lecture or a sermon or a political discourse, but to share in a duty, both personal and collective, revealed to them by the story of Emmaus, and the existence among them of the poor in their own small town, in the rest of France, throughout the world.

Then women pulled off their rings and their earrings, and the men got out their money, and put their names down on the com-mittees' lists.

Sometimes after these talks young men, shaken by his words, would collect round him and say: 'Father, our parents will be organizing committees and finding lodging for the homeless, but we would like to start from scratch, we would like to live like you, try to save people, set up communities. How should we begin?'

He would reply:

'If it is not just a chivalrous instinct which inspires you, if you are responding to some profound need in the depths of your soul, then go and put up a tent outside the town, and begin to cultivate a manure heap. The first poor devil to come and work with you will get drunk. The second and the third will fight each other, the fourth will rob you, perhaps the fifth will hate you and try to kill you. By then, you will either have had enough, and you will give up, or you will stick it out. Perhaps you will save the sixth man, and then it will all have been worth while.'

He returned to Paris hurriedly, shut himself into his little room at the Rochester with the leaders of the organization, with the financiers and Government representatives. Sometimes he was so worn out that he received them lying on his bed.

Spring was on its way. The killing frosts were over. Flowers appeared. Soon the nightmare days would be forgotten. In a few short weeks, people would wonder what lunacy had made them concern themselves so generously with the poor, what strange impulse had led them on frosty nights to the Butte Ste Geneviève, in love, and anger, and an orgy of charity.

A few short weeks, and the newspapers would be tired of publishing articles about the campaign for solidarity, or the lists of tragic cases needing help. A new star would replace the Abbé Pierre on the front page—the spring. 'Why talk about misery? There is none any more, it's all been put right. The fine days are here, and we did our duty during the dark ones, so let us forget about it.'

Among the hundreds of pictures of the Abbé, there was a coloured photograph of him kissing a little girl in a red shawl. In many homes this picture was cut out, framed, and hung on the wall. This popular picture would one day rot on the walls, become torn and neglected.

But to perpetuate his memory the walls were going up at Plessis-Trévise. The Abbé made hurried visits to the workshops, then left for the other end of France. And he thought as he sat in his compartment how one must 'strike while the iron is hot'; one must repeat that gifts would not solve the problem, but only a change in the way things were run, and in the will of those running them, and by an attack of bad conscience on the part of both State and public.

He went abroad, to England, Belgium and Switzerland, wearing himself out. He considered launching a journal to defend the causes for which he lived, and which should be called *The Voice of the Voiceless*.

My book was now displayed in bookshop windows, this book which owed everything to Emmaus. I signed copies, in the midst of milling crowds, under the flash-bulbs of Press photographers, beneath the eye of the television camera. A strange and touching task, an unaccustomed rôle to which luck or Providence had destined me. But it was an usurped fame.

When I moved from place to place, the newspapers quoted my name. But in Neuilly, Pomponne, Plessis-Trévise, those whose story I had told continued their obscure work as before. Their ragpicker-builders still slept in tents, in caravans, in barracks, and scratched in the filth in all weathers; unloaded scrap-iron and laid cement blocks. This ephemeral fame did not change their way of life. Journalists, ministers, and others anxious to see them, came in droves to their workshops, and the men of Emmaus, irritated by their attentions, continued to unload scrap-iron, to scratch among the filth, to lay cement blocks. They thought to themselves: 'We are not in a zoo. Leave us to work in peace.' They scarcely read the papers, and if in the evenings the wireless brought them echoes of their glory, they preferred not to listen. 'That's enough—switch to another station.'

3

THE BOGUS SOCIAL WORKER

'ANTOINE COMES here occasionally. He is one of the people responsible for the Liège Metro shelter.' So Marie-France, a voluntary worker at the Rochester, told me.

She spoke in non-committal tones. For the first time, she was not smiling this morning. Her pleasant face was pale, as if she were afraid. She was shivering, despite the dry heat of the radiators, which were going full blast in this office set up in a bedroom at the Hotel Rochester.

'You're absolutely worn out, Marie-France,' I said to her. 'You're feverish.'

'It's not that,' she said, shrugging her shoulders.

Suddenly her eyes widened as if, instead of me, she saw another presence which terrified her. Her two small fists went up to her forehead, and she said through clenched teeth: 'Oh, the horrible woman!'

The office was always sending notes to the Press, warning people to be on their guard against the numerous crooks who collected money ostensibly for the homeless. Marie-France had hitherto paid little attention to these. Thieves, bogus priests, sellers of postcards, beggars, reduced to such expedients by distress—why had they not appealed to Emmaus which would have helped them? As late as yesterday, she had been tempted to feel sorry for them, those poor wretches who had not yet realized that the world had become good, and that we were living in a new age, where everyone would have his share according to his needs.

Well—now she knew—her eyes were open to the horrible truth. Poverty was widespread and always would be, and evil was everywhere. After the first shock, the world would once more become a desert of selfishness, a jungle where in the struggle to live, the most cynical, the most cunning, the most ferocious, would triumph.

Marie-France was only twenty. The daughter of the director of a big store, she had always lived in a middle-class environment, preserved from the wickedness of the world. Moved by a generous impulse after hearing the Abbé's appeal, she came to offer her services, and for seventeen days she had been filing the evidence of generosity and distress alike. The world of poverty was revealed to her, but not yet the world of wickedness.

During these seventeen days, she had hardly slept or left the office, the window of which looked out on to a courtyard and the blind, grey walls of buildings. The electric light, on from morning till night, tried her eyes, and the air was thick with the cigarette smoke of her overworked colleagues. The telephone rang continually. The post arrived with sackfuls of correspondence which had to be sorted, classified, and indexed. For the first ten days she only had a bedside table for a desk, and she filed her cards in two cardboard shoeboxes on the ground: in the right, offers of lodgings, in the left, requests for the same. Later, the working conditions improved—she had a wooden table out of a restaurant, on trestles, with a brand of beer inscribed on it in big letters. She loved this office, her work, the strange uplifting atmosphere of this place.

It was always with the same thrill that she tore open with her paper-knife the envelopes from distant villages, from abroad, removed the letter, and with tears in her eyes deciphered the clumsy handwriting.

'Dear Father, I am five years old—since I did not cry at the dentist, I have been given fifty francs, which I send to you with a kiss from Lucien.'

Or:

'Mummy promised me a bicycle which pleased me very much, but I am almost as glad for the money to go to some unhappy child. Lucie, aged 10.'

Or:

'Dear Father, I am 70, at the almshouse of C. I have given up smoking because I am ashamed to think how much I have spent on tobacco in my life, money which could have saved people less fortunate than me. I send you 350 francs.'

Or:

'Dear Father, My communist friends and myself of Cell N do not share your ideas, but what you are doing for the victims of society is good. So we send you a subscription of 1500 francs.'

She entered up and handed over the letters and the money to her colleague, kept the offers of lodging which she indexed on numbered cards. The best letters would be forwarded to the Abbé Pierre.

'How good it is to fight all together like this against evil,' she thought, as she recorded on other cards the lamentable cases described in some of the letters:

'Mrs. E. has lost three children. The five still living are threatened with tuberculosis. The husband is a labourer and has chronic bronchitis. They sleep four in a bed, in a damp room. They are to be evicted in two months' time.'

'Mrs. F. Ill. Mother of four—earns 28,000 francs a month. Pays 18,000 rent per month—the rest is mortgaged to pay off a loan.'

'Mrs. L. Widow since the First World War. Recently came out of hospital. She and her grandson cannot find lodgings.'

'Miss L. No father—lives in a wooden shack exposed to the weather. The rain comes in through gaps in the planks. Her mother is ill and bedridden.'

She drew out from the card index of offers of lodging Offer No. 89: 'I live alone in a four-roomed flat, and am willing to give up two of my rooms to a family.'

'It's untrue that the world is wicked and selfish,' thought Marie-
France. 'God is good, and I thank him for his presence at these
cross-roads of salvation. You only have to reveal suffering, as the
Abbé Pierre has done, for hearts to open; they can all be saved by
these offers of lodging, and by the money enclosed in the letters.
During the early days of the appeal, 1,000- and 10,000-franc notes
were scattered over the desks, left by anonymous donors, but no
one out of all the crowds in the office ever touched them. What
better proof is there that men's hearts have changed?'

Thus, for seventeen days and almost as many nights, in impossible working conditions, Marie-France stayed at her post and
smiled despite her extreme exhaustion.

But on the seventeenth day she saw the enemy, and then she
flinched. For the first time, she saw evil with its cunning icy mask;
and the worst of it was that she did not recognize it for what it
was. She smiled at it and became its unwitting accomplice.

Evil is something quite different from misfortune. Misfortune
is blind, but evil is conscious. Misfortune is a thing, but evil is a
living enemy. Floods, avalanches, fires, cold spells, are misfor-
tunes against which one can fight righteously, as all France was
doing, with Marie-France at the centre of the struggle.

Two days before, she was alone in the office when a respectable-
looking lady was announced. She stood there, upright, dignified,
with her white hair, her grey tailor-made resembling the Red
Cross uniform. She said she came from the Assistance Board: 'I
look after a very populous district, a city of hovels. There is grave
danger from tuberculosis, and the girls are also threatened with
another danger—drunken fathers, half-demented mothers. One
of the tenements has been declared insanitary, and the families who
live in it are to be put on the street. I have tried in vain to house
them. I wrote to the Mayor, the Prefecture, the Ministry, but
there is no room for them anywhere.'

Whereupon Marie-France searched frantically in her files for
offers of lodging. Of course she should have waited till Patrice
returned and asked his advice. She should have made inquiries,

but Marie-France couldn't wait. The thought of those people thrown out! And the rain coming down! And the lady had been so insistent.

'Here. Take these ten or twelve addresses of people offering lodging.'

Marie-France gave her the cards and in doing so noticed the name of the last one—an address quite near where she herself lived.

The next morning she passed this house and went in to witness the happiness of a family which had been saved, and to thank their benefactress. The latter received her with cold looks.

'I took them in,' she said, 'and gave them two rooms. I don't wish to cry over it now, but I don't intend to do it again.'

'What's the matter?'

'Go and talk to them.'

Marie-France knocked at their door. You have to ignore the ingratitude of poor people; they have suffered so much, their hearts even more than their bodies are worn out by poverty, and the little you can do for them now cannot compensate for the huge arrears of injustice—nevertheless . . .

'And there's no running water,' said the mother sharply.

'It can't be helped,' answered Marie-France, 'you must make do for the time being with what you have been given.'

'Given!' cried the woman. 'Given! You call a down payment of 25,000 francs a gift? We had to borrow it at 10 per cent.'

'What 25,000 francs?'

'Don't act like an innocent. The lady demanded 25,000 francs for giving us this address.' The address given by Marie-France to the bogus social worker.

She ran back to the office, consulted her lists and went off again. Each of the twelve families lodged had paid 25,000 to 50,000 francs, huge sums which they had to raise hurriedly by selling clothes and furniture, for rooms offered free by the owners. This so-called social assistance worker had not left her name, no one knew who she was. She must have obtained the addresses of those who were badly housed through personal inquiries at town halls, and so on, and through advertisements in the papers.

So Marie-France asked her parents for the money against her dowry, and repaid the unfortunate people. She wanted to repair the damage, but one can never undo the effects of evil. Something always remains. In Marie-France's case it was disgust and fear. Henceforth the world no longer felt safe, and she smiled less often.

But she went on with her work, opening the envelopes as they arrived.

'We are not well off, we have three children, and we live in three rooms, but we can squeeze up, and welcome a family.'

'I am an old woman of 84, ill and alone. I have seen much, suffered greatly. I write just to tell you not to get discouraged.'

Gradually Marie-France recovered her peace and confidence. It is true that evil exists, and one must realize the fact in order to appreciate generosity at its true value.

4

CHARITY'S DON QUIXOTE

IT WAS a warm little room, with a polished floor, well arranged, and full of peace and sunshine. The old lady, the mother of my friend Ernest, sighed as she sat in her green velvet armchair, from which for thirty years she had watched the street as she knitted.

'I never get any sleep now—he used to be so quiet. But now he is demented, as if there was no such thing as charity before he came along.'

Her son answered gravely:

'I repeat, Mama, it is not a question of charity, but of justice.'

'He keeps on telling me that—justice—that's the word all right. It got you into prison. And now I hardly dare go out. The whole street is talking about you.'

'You mustn't be ashamed, Mama. I'm proud to have been in prison by mistake.'

'You haven't heard the worst of it. They nearly sacked you from the office.'

Ernest's voice, sad and pleading, said: 'Ten days' absence, that was nothing very terrible, and when I explained, Monsieur Dutout congratulated me.'

But his mother was merciless.

'He congratulated you, oh yes. The hero, the martyr of justice, the Don Quixote of Charity.'

Ernest got to his feet so abruptly that he knocked over the chair.

'I'm ashamed of nothing!' he cried. 'Of nothing! Do you hear?'

The old lady groaned and beat her hands against her head.

'That's what he's like now,' she wailed. 'As if I hadn't always done everything to make his life easy and quiet. Can *you* understand how, at the age of forty-three, he can suddenly start chasing adventures? Try to make him see reason. Every night he goes out. He's up to something, but I don't know what.'

Ernest, I might have said, was not one of his mother's goldfish in a bowl, though for forty years she had treated him as such. He had lived in a prison, whose invisible walls were order, discipline, selfishness—it was an air-conditioned retreat against the rough winds of the world. But a fortnight before, at noon, a ray of daylight percolated through, when a voice on the radio said: 'I need your help, my friends.' Ernest had got up, heart beating fast, beads of sweat on his brow, and murmured: 'I'm off.'

'But it's not time yet for the office,' said his mother, who was a little deaf.

Ernest went out half an hour early. The era of disorder had begun.

His old mother besought me to help her catch the fish and put it back in the bowl. 'Reason with him. All the time I'm terrified of some new outburst.'

She proceeded to tell me the story of his first breakaway.

'On the night of February the 1st,' she said, 'he went off, without having eaten, to rent the wheelbarrow belonging to the wine, wood and coal merchant, to collect bread straight from the bakeries for the Abbé Pierre's poor. That was his wonderful idea. In our district. Just like a beggar. They gave of course, but more mouldy bread than fresh. He went right across Paris pushing his wheelbarrow, to lay his harvest at the feet of the Abbé Pierre at the Hotel Rochester. Do you think the Abbé was there to thank him? But he met this Patrice, a boy who looked after the food arrangements for the refugees, or something of the sort.

'And each day, each evening, he made this exhausting tour

with his ridiculous wheelbarrow, collecting clothing, food, bed-clothes, shoes, pots and pans. He even went so far as to pick up old papers to sell to a second-hand shop. He took the money to the Rochester. He was doing his own particular ragpicking, like the ragpickers of Emmaus.

'As a result of this he became ill, and took a week off from the office—but do you imagine he stayed in bed? No. On the third day, when he was still feverish, he took the train to Valence where his brother lives. He took with him another inspired idea, and also the gramophone record made by the Abbé Pierre. He rented a banqueting room at a café, and designed posters with which he placarded the town, inscribed in his own handwriting: "Lecture on the new revolution of solidarity in Paris. Proceeds to be given to the homeless—by Ernest B., an Emmaus volunteer." Yes—he put our name, our family name, on those posters.'

The old lady laid down her knitting for a moment and looked over her spectacles at her guilty son. Then the infuriated clicking began once more.

But I did not smile. In imagination I heard his voice, half stammering, half shouting, and his speech devoid of order and style, like the public confession of someone picked up by the Salvation Army.

'I believed in nothing and led an empty life. Now I live by Faith. I was only a speck of dust, but I thought I was the centre of the world. I have learned the truth, which is that if our life is filled with love for our neighbours, and is devoted to our weakest brethren, we are no longer dust, but a particle of God's own light.'

Ernest told the story of the 'revolt' of the 1st of February, and of his own humble part in it. And the bourgeois of Valence, who every Sunday used to doze through their curé's sermons on charity, as they listened to that unpractised voice felt something come to life within them, something true and exalting.

Ernest's powers of conviction derived from the fact that his words witnessed to an action, to something done, on however modest a scale. He collected 35,000 francs. The next day he went on to a neighbouring town, where he once more gave his talk.

At the end of the week, having given four lectures, he was packing to return to Paris when two plain-clothes police officers knocked at the door.

'Have you got an authorization to collect money? Have you been sent by Emmaus?'

'No, I have no authority. I'm doing this on my own initiative.'

At the police station they rang Paris. The Abbé Pierre had never heard of Ernest B. Crooks were numerous in Paris and the provinces, collecting for the homeless, and the scandal had to be stopped, and an example made.

Ernest protested in vain. He was arrested and taken back to Paris between two policemen, and sent to prison, where his mother came weeping to visit him. He stayed there eight days. A paragraph in the papers about this criminal Ernest happened to catch the eye of his friend Patrice, who rushed to the Abbé Pierre to plead his cause and to guarantee his honesty. The Abbé immediately leapt into his car and drove to the Palais de Justice. And as soon as he saw Ernest he had no doubts whatever.

'I hope you've no grudge against me,' he said, 'but I didn't know you.'

Now there only remained for my friend the most difficult part of all, to overcome his mother's lack of understanding, and to emerge from childhood.

'In that escapade Ernest only involved himself,' continued his mother, 'but the affair of the secret tenant disturbed the peace and safety of our whole block of flats.

'On that very first evening, Ernest hid a secret tenant in the attic belonging to the ladies on the sixth door. He brought off this coup with the help of Raoul, the son of one of these ladies. This young scout was on duty with his troop near the Refuge de la Butte on this notorious 1st of February. I can understand a boy of twelve getting excited over that sort of thing, but Ernest is forty-three. After his bread-collecting round was over, Ernest was on his way back from the Rochester about 10 p.m. and was still dragging his wheelbarrow after him as he passed by the Butte. That is where he met you, I think. When he left you he noticed, among a group of campers-out who had been unearthed from beneath the bridges, a poor fellow, an advertisement tout or something of the kind, and there and then he offered him a room. And where, if you please? Here, in his home, in my home, in our home. Imagine it at half-past twelve at night! Ernest and the scout in uniform pushing the poor wretch in the wheelbarrow, where he did not know, all three worn out with cold, exhausted, their hearts overflowing with love for one another. Home they came!'

The old lady's ironical tone was not due to malevolence or cynicism, but simply jealousy of her son's new object of affection, of the loving-kindness which was continually involving him in new adventures. Ernest was upset by her lack of understanding, but it also served to nourish his new sense of vocation. He did not mind looking ridiculous, he accepted the responsibility of his acts, and only refused to deny himself and give up.

The old lady continued her recital in a monotonous voice, with occasional outbursts of malice.

When they reached the entrance to the block of flats, their exaltation had somewhat diminished. Ernest could only put up the stranger by giving him his own bed. Then the scout remembered the attic, an empty servant's room, belonging to his mother and used as a rubbish room. It contained a rug and a mattress. They crept upstairs, forced the lock, and installed the secret lodger, about whom they knew nothing. He said his name was Pierre, and that he went the rounds of the shops for a second-rate agency, canvassing unlikely commissions for advertisements. As he didn't earn enough for a hotel room, he slept in the street, at the risk of catching his death. Actually he was a gentle creature, shy and clean, with a spark of gaiety and courage not yet extinguished by poverty.

The servant's room was just above the ladies' sixth-floor flat. Raoul's family consisted of his mother, an officer's widow, his aunt, and his elder sister Isabel! A Protestant family, austere but not without feelings, though perhaps not strong enough to admit the propriety of forcing the lock of their attic to lodge a clandestine tenant. So Raoul kept quiet and trembled when each evening about nine o'clock he heard their protégé passing along the landing as he climbed the staircase towards the attic. Despite the precaution of carrying his shoes, creaking could be heard in the garret just above the dining-room where the gloomy meal was just finishing.

On the fourth day, the aunt looked up. 'There are rats up there —we must put some poison down.'

However, it was Isabel who first discovered him. On going up to the attic one night to look for a rug, she saw the light from a candle between the planks forming the partition. Mastering her terror, she opened the door and saw the young man, rolled up in rugs and smoking a cigarette. He was reading by the candlelight a detective story lent him by Raoul. There was a long silence, during which the two young people, each more scared than the other, regarded one another.

The next morning Isabel secretly took up a bowl of soup. The stranger had not mentioned that Raoul was involved, with the result that Isabel, like her brother, thought she alone knew the secret. During meals, each grew pale as they heard the footsteps of their protégé regaining his hideout. They began to talk in loud voices to distract the attention of the other three at table.

On the sixth day, there was a chance meeting on the landing of the aunt and the young man, who passed her, shoes in hand, on the way up to the attic.

'Where are you going to like that, young man?' asked the aunt.

'To sleep—I am very tired,' he whispered confidentially.

And falteringly, balancing to and fro on stockinged feet, he confessed his rôle of squatter, and begged for mercy. In a few days' time he would be leaving and would be going back on the road.

The old maid's heart was filled with pity. The romantic aspect of the affair enchanted her. She promised to keep his secret, and the next day the boy found on his return hot soup and biscuits.

Some days went by, and every night three pairs of ears listened for the light step, and three pairs of eyes were raised towards the ceiling, while three hearts beat faster for fear that the rest of the family would discover the secret. The mother raised her eyebrows in surprise at the animated discourse of her children and her elder sister, their senseless laughter, their coughing, their hasty incoherent conversation.

All comes to him who waits: the mother also discovered the secret. One Sunday morning, the rest of the family went off to church. Not feeling very well, she remained behind. She heard footsteps overhead. There was no mistake. They came from the attic. She seized her husband's revolver and went upstairs. She found the young man who had been having a late lie-in tidying up the attic.

After a preliminary moment of stupefaction, this determined lady, who lacked neither charity nor a sense of humour, invited the boy to come down to the kitchen for a cup of coffee.

'My sister and children knew you were up there? Why didn't they say anything?'

'They were afraid, perhaps.'

'That's a nice thing! Afraid of me!'

She didn't turn the boy out. She gave him the run of the attic. But for fun and a little for revenge, she determined not to tell the others that she knew, and to watch their behaviour when their guest returned that night. She decided to make a few remarks which would add to their confusion and anxiety, such as, 'There must be a very large rat upstairs—can't you hear it? Perhaps it is a man. I shall telephone the police.'

But she never had the chance to play her little comedy. That night there was no familiar footstep. In vain Raoul and the ladies listened. The ceiling was dumb. They delayed going to bed on various pretexts, and till late in the night, unable to sleep, they lay, eyes open, ears listening, awaiting the return of their mysterious guest. And they felt sad and disillusioned, as when a friend has let one down.

About 2 a.m. the aunt woke suddenly, as at last she heard footsteps above her head. On the staircase she collided with Raoul in pyjamas, who was on his way down from the attic after assuring himself that it was empty. Their whispered explanations on the staircase woke Isabel who by opening the door woke her mother.

Ernest's mother paused. I was as impatient as a child for her to continue. 'But that's not the end of the story?' I queried. 'Didn't he come back?'

She shrugged her shoulders, gave a little laugh and resumed.

'Imagine the three women in nightdresses and dressing-gowns, and their boy in pyjamas, discussing in whispers on the landing, and shivering with cold.'

Gradually the discussion became a quarrel. 'You should have told me,' said the mother to the aunt. 'The poor boy was freezing up there. Children who do not trust their mother——'

'You terrorize them,' said the aunt.

'What will the boy think of us, and the other tenants when they hear the story?'

Suddenly they heard the front door open and footsteps climbing up. The anxious faces suddenly relaxed, four of them looking over the banisters, smiling, as they watched their friend come up the stairs.

'Well,' I said, 'it seems . . .'

'That all's well that ends well,' cried the old lady vivaciously, as if she were only waiting for me to speak to reach the climax of the tale. 'It is at this point that the story really begins. Here we have this man, whom nobody knows, introduced to those ladies living alone, putting down roots in their home. What will happen if he is a bad character, or a maniac, or a thief?'

'You must not look for the worst in everything,' said Ernest. 'Pierre is a decent chap.'

'Understand this. Charity is dangerous. It creates disorders. There is something cursed about it.'

'Be quiet!' cried Ernest. 'What you're saying is monstrous.'

'No, it is not, and one day you will realize.'

I felt suddenly sad and discouraged. It is true that charity is difficult; often the people for whom we have sacrificed time and money give us nothing in exchange but suffering. It is true that charity is dangerous and creates disorder in our lives. But every life is only justified by service, and the willingness to share good fortune.

I took my leave. Ernest accompanied me to the door. 'If it would amuse you,' he said bitterly, 'I could also tell you the story of the President. My mother does not know about it—if she did she would make an awful fuss. When we were doing a collection in our street, I persuaded the wife of the President of the Treasury Court to let me clear out her attic. Her husband was away. A week later he rang our doorbell furiously—I had removed from his attic, together with his love-letters from the time of his engagement, a valuable set of *Charivari*, a satirical periodical of the last century. He willingly abandoned his love-letters, but demanded that his reviews be returned to him. Meantime, I had sold all the papers to the rag-and-bone man, and left the money at the Rochester. The rag-and-bone man had delivered his stock to a pulp-mill. What could I do? The only solution was to look for a similar collection among the bargain bookstalls, or the antique shops, and curio shops. I was about to put an advertisement in the paper, when I found what I wanted at a stall on the Left Bank which offered me the set for 20,000 francs. That's a lot of money for me.'

Suddenly he said: 'Come on,' and dragged me quickly across the square, which was surrounded by blocks of flats. One of these was unfinished. Huge advertisement hoardings covered the steel and concrete skeleton of the façade.

'The owners prefer not to finish it. They earn more by renting the site for those advertisement hoardings than they would get from the tenants.'

Further on a narrow passageway led to a damp and foetid little courtyard. There was no light in the dark decrepit old building, and several windows had broken panes of glass.

'This house has been empty for fifteen years,' said Ernest. 'With a few repairs it could be made habitable. I know more than a dozen families out on the streets. There are more than a thousand requests for homes in the files of the Rochester.'

We retraced our footsteps to the square.

'Do you think I've wasted my time during this last week since I came out of prison? I have learnt a few things, such as that you can never count on public organizations. I am no longer working alone. We have set up the nucleus of a committee of three friends, with Pierre D. and old Louis. I'll introduce you to them, they know what it is like to be on the streets. We'll get important people in the district to join the committee.'

On the street corner he pushed open the door of a little wine, wood and coal shop, kept by a man from Auvergne. The shop was only a narrow passage; on one side, the counter with bottles and casks, on the other, a row of minute tables. The owner, a big jovial man, held out his hand.

'Well, Monsieur Ernest, and when is this squatting going to start?'

'Not so fast. The day after tomorrow I am going to see an architect and ask him to inspect the house and tell us if it is habitable.'

5

HOW OLD LOUIS WOKE UP

'THE WORST thing about poverty,' said old Louis to me
next day in the shop of the man from Auvergne, 'is that
you get used to it. It's like a drug. You slide into a state
of trance, through physical weakness, through the habit of
despair. You cease to read. What's the use? You've given up
your dignity, your self-respect. You no longer care about people's
contempt. You fall asleep for life, and it seems to me that after
being a tramp for thirteen years, I am only just waking up.

'Once I was a blacksmith, then came the war and illness, ruin,
solitude. I was off on the roads. I'm going to tell you about the
night of the 1st of February, when I woke up after thirteen years
of sleep.'

On the night of February 1st he went to sleep at eleven o'clock
wrapped in his old military overcoat, on the grating of the Underground at Rue des Deux-Boules, with his haversack beneath his
head. From 3 a.m. onwards the lorries laden with cauliflowers
began to arrive, and it was these he used to help to unload. He
had been feeling unwell for several days past. His sleep was
feverish and broken by coughing. Suddenly a hand shook him
gently by the shoulder. The odour of spring penetrated his
dreams. In a white fur coat, an angel was bending over him and
murmuring: 'My friend, you will catch cold; don't stay there—
come—we are going to put you in a shelter.'

He was wrong to say 'Go to hell' to the perfumed angel, but
he didn't have the strength to get to his feet and follow her. And

the car was too beautiful. Out of the corner of his eye he saw a
bumper in massive silver.

'I am sorry, I am ill. I don't want to help you to save your soul,
madame. So nuts to you. It's not a nice word, but you should
console yourself by thinking that folks like me don't deserve the
help of people like you.'

The car went off, and Louis went back to sleep. But not for
long. Two police officers dragged him from his slumbers. It was
the first time for a month they had bothered with the homeless
other than to make them move on. They too were dragging
through the dark streets their little burden of shame. It was a new
voice they had heard, issuing not from a robot in uniform, but
from the human heart.

'Mustn't stay there, old man, you'll die.'

'I've got my papers on me.'

'We're not asking for your papers. Come to the police station.'

'What do you want with me?'

'We'll give you a hot drink.'

Louis went with them, so as not to be disobliging or to upset
their temporary goodwill. Who knew what their reactions would
be the following day when they woke up from this strange access
of shamefacedness?

At the police station, a dozen or so 'customers' were warming
themselves: two tramps, five young labourers and students, two
Algerians, an old actor in desperate straits, two women, and a
couple of old men. They were sitting on benches around the
stove. They were all silent, petrified by the fraternal solicitude of
the policemen, who were making hot drinks.

Just as they were being served, the door opened and a large man
wearing a duffle coat, riding-breeches and boots, a retired officer
type, followed by two or three others, called out to the police the
absurd words: 'The Charity Commandos!'

The students burst out laughing.

'How many have you got here?'

'About a dozen.'

'Fine. We'll take them with us. It's all set. Let's go.'

The police let them go, thankful to be rid of them.

They were put into four cars. Louis got in with a nice fellow, some sort of official, in a four-cylinder Citroën, at the tail-end of the cavalcade. The little car kept up with difficulty, and the driver was afraid of losing the rest. They went along the quays, up two or three little streets, then stopped in front of a church. A priest with his housekeeper and his curate welcomed them at the door of the presbytery, a very old, very touching little priest. He took them into a dining-room, where a table fit for a wedding banquet was laid.

'You are God's poor,' he said, 'and I welcome you—if belatedly. It is very late in the day that I open my door to poverty. I ask your pardon. Eat and drink.'

He too, the lady, the police, and the commandos, were not proud of themselves in the presence of Louis and the others, and Louis felt ashamed at upsetting all these people who had always lived in peace and comfort.

When they had all eaten and drunk, served by the priest, his housekeeper and the gentlemen of the commando, and the atmosphere had thawed out a little, the old actor wanted to thank them by singing one of his former successes: *Nini the Dogskin* by Bruant. But the chief commando said it was too late. They must sleep.

Louis thought of his work in the market and of the arrival of the cauliflower lorries. But this was a strange mad night, and stupefied by fever and also a little drunk, he followed the adventure to the end. They got back into the cars. The procession set off again with the little Citroën behind, along the Seine to the Place Mauberge and La Montagne. The tent was crammed full, so they went to find another shelter. The town hall of this sixth arrondissement was full also. So off they went again, but at the place where the Rue de Grenelle crosses the Boulevard Raspail, the Citroën lost touch with the others.

'How annoying,' said the driver to Louis, who was dozing. 'I really don't know what to do. I can't take you to my home. What would my wife say? I shall get you into a hotel.'

Both hotels they called at were full.

Finally Louis felt sorry for him, and begged him to leave him anywhere in the street.

'No, no, at least at a police station.'

They were by now so far from the market that Louis did not dare ask to be driven there. The car stopped near a police post. The two men shook hands. The driver gave Louis 500 francs and departed.

But Louis did not go into the post. He preferred to walk along the icy street, keeping close to the wall for shelter from the wind. He found a niche in a doorway and squeezed himself into it, sighing: 'Peace at last.' But not for long. A young man returning all lit-up from a reunion of his political group, shook him and woke him by the vehemence of his triumphant indignation.

'So the famous Abbé has forgotten you, brother? All this to-do over the rescue of a few sub-proles, with full government publicity, is really only a manœuvre to sidetrack popular fury and indignation. Say, aren't I right, comrade?'

Louis coughed and growled: 'Yes, yes.' He was too tired to feel anger and indignation, or to start an argument. The young man continued the conversation, shaking him by the strap of his haversack.

'Charity is like a plaster over a crumbling building. What is pity? Another opium of the people—only justice is any good. I don't agree with the idea of individual acts of charity, comrade, but I can't let you collapse out of doors.'

And he took Louis to his home. In order not to wake his parents, he told Louis not to cough, and to take off his shoes on the stairs. He put Louis in his own little room, in his own bed, and while preparing to sleep on the floor himself, he continued to whisper his dialectic till he fell asleep in the middle of a sentence.

But Louis could not close an eye. He sweated and shivered at the same time, and breathed with difficulty. So as to be able to cough freely, he got up quietly and, shoes in hand, went back downstairs into the street. Six a.m. The percolators were beginning to hiss in the little cafés. Louis had a rum, but did not linger over it. He walked slowly towards the market. Perhaps with a bit of luck there would still be some work for him. But his shoes felt like lead, and there was a great weight on his chest. Stupefied with cold, lack of sleep and fever, he stopped to get his breath, and sat down on the cover of a dustbin. An old shoemaker walked past, in his hand a little aluminium can in which he fetched his milk each day from the creamery. He saw Louis swaying about on the dustbin, about to fall.

'Drunk so early?' growled the shoemaker.

But Louis looked up at him in a mute appeal for help.

'But you're ill,' said the shoemaker. 'Come inside for a moment and get warm.'

' "For a moment": that's what he said. But I've been there for a month. Every morning I say: "Alphonse, I must go." He curses me and says he's still got things for me to do, that I owe him that much at least, to help him. For three weeks he's looked after me, I don't know why. Need me? Why, while he hammers on toes and heels, I run errands for him, do the shopping and the cooking. We get on well together; we don't talk much, and I would like nothing better than to stay there, but I don't want to eat him out of house and home, so I shall go back to work in the market tomorrow. Each day I earn a little, and bring back carrots and cabbages for the midday soup.[1] They'll give them to me for nothing in the spring. Perhaps I'll go and work on a farm. I have to be free—I must get away. But friendship is also important. What do you think? And I don't know which of us needs the other most. Talking of need, it is not only Alphonse who needs me. There are hundreds of people to whom I could be useful. Yes, sir. Tell Monsieur Ernest he can count on me a hundred per cent. And he can count on Alphonse too. Tell him so from time to

[1] This is all the French working man has for his midday meal. *Translator.*

time. It will do him good to hear it. We are not alone in the world. That is what I have learnt. There are always others who are worse off than ourselves. Whole families, children. If we are good for something we must prove it without waiting too long. And make life, in our own little corner, less ugly and painful. I tell you I've woken up and I have no wish to go to sleep again.'

6

THE BADOROU FAMILY

I WAS LIVING at the time with a friend, Julien Verdier, a movie actor, in a flat belonging to a Mademoiselle X. We got to know one another, and this charming lady told me her story.

She lived alone on the third floor with her dog, in a nine-roomed flat which she had always refused to sub-let, and where she lovingly cared for her beautiful furniture and heirlooms from her aristocratic family. In the flat, her parents and grandparents had lived and died.

On the 2nd or 3rd of February, her nephew Jeannot, burning with zeal, had knocked on her door and told her it was her duty to be hospitable to the homeless. The lady had heard about the Abbé Pierre and admired him greatly. She was also a good Christian, and had sent him a thousand francs. But it had never occurred to her that his appeals were addressed to her. Her empty flat, with nine rooms, a temple of memories, bore no relation to this business. She herself only used two rooms and the kitchen. The other rooms, uninhabited for thirty years, without electric light or heating, with shut windows and drawn blinds, belonged to the moths and worms and her memories. And when Jeannot made her feel ashamed of her egoism, she showed him the door. But that night she did not sleep. The young man's words, confirming the articles in the papers and the appeals on the radio, gradually penetrated the shell of exclusiveness and the egoism mingled with the sacred memory of her parents and an almost

superstitious attachment to possessions. That night, candlestick
in hand, she toured the seven cold empty rooms, where she never
went except to 'raise the dust'. She cast loving glances at the
carpets, furniture, pictures, candelabra, knick-knacks. She suddenly felt lonely, at a loss, shivering from some obscure anguish.
She realized that these rooms and their contents had been too long
given up to the dead. They wanted to come alive, to serve a
purpose. The rooms, furthermore, badly needed repairing: the
stucco was peeling off, the ceilings were cracking, the door hinges
had come unstuck. A possible tenant could do up the rooms in
exchange for hospitality. In the ninth and last room, the smallest,
there was a wash-basin.

The next day she gave her nephew a letter to give to the Abbé
Pierre.

'You're in the movement, so give him this letter. I'm offering
a room to a deserving family, if possible to a working painter and
decorator, in exchange for work.'

Jeannot replied that true charity admits of no restrictions or
working conditions, and ran to the Rochester. Being unable to
see the Abbé himself, he gave the letter to his friend Patrice.

That same evening the Badorou family rang the old lady's doorbell: a husband and wife and three children, aged from four to
seven years. They were Gascons, simple folk, who had sold their
small flat in Toulouse and their possessions to come to Paris,
hoping to find better accommodation and work. They had been
waiting three days in the basement of the Rochester. The father
was a painter and decorator, a decent fellow, but a trifle bohemian
in his habits, a great talker and not very reliable, really more of a
handy man than a skilled workmen. His wife was like him, a
fat soft careless creature, good-natured, uninhibited, incapable
of economizing or of being what Mademoiselle X called
'serious'.

Before long there was a resounding clash of temperaments between Mademoiselle X and her guests, whose children played
football in the big drawing-room, and teased the dog. Mademoi-

selle X, set in her ways, resented doors being left open, and the
entire flat being used as a playground, when in fact the Badorous
had only been given the small room with the wash-basin. She
decided to complain to the Abbé Pierre in person, for she had not
the courage to turn them out herself.

She went first to the Rochester, then to Neuilly-Plaisance.
Finally the taxi put her down, in the rain, in the forest at the
entrance to the Pomponnette encampment. Other cars had stopped in the muddy clearings; an official visit was being paid by the
Prefect who, with the Mayor and journalists, was groping about
in the mud in the wake of the Abbé Pierre, between huts, sheds,
tents, caravans and the carcasses of old motor-buses. From behind
their windows, and on the thresholds of their huts, women and
children silently watched them go past.

The Prefect murmured, as his predecessor, the Minister, had
done: 'How is this possible? I had no idea.'

The Abbé Pierre answered: 'In your offices and on paper, you
have all the arguments, but here on the spot we always win the
day.'

Mademoiselle X trotted along in the mud behind the procession, and lowered her eyes beneath the glances of these children,
who so much resembled the Badorou children.

On the spot charity always wins, and Mademoiselle X got back
into her taxi, without having approached the Abbé Pierre, without
telling him about the petty conflicts with her tenants. Incidents
which had seemed intolerable in Paris lost their importance here.
The important thing was to live, and not to be mean, nor to
condemn the Badorous to the life of Pomponnette.

On the way home she thought about all this, and decided that
however little God grants us, it is a gratuitous favour and is
always sufficient. Seven rooms are sufficient. Five or three are
enough to live in. The chance to succour and shelter a family was
a favour for which she ought to thank God. And for having
revealed to her in time the purpose of her life, she thanked Him,
unable to restrain her tears.

In the spring, the Badorous, like migrant birds, went back to the South. After they had gone they left the doors open, both those of the flat and those of Mademoiselle X's heart, open for other families who were waiting outside. But how many other apartments remained shut, and how many hearts?

7

THE DEATH OF THE 'LIÈGE'

A T THE end of February, the police, 'to maintain order',
closed the emergency shelters which had been set up during
the great cold wave in the underground stations, town
halls, schools and banqueting halls. The buildings were to revert
to their original purpose, and all the afflicted persons whom they
had housed were sent back on to the streets, or parked outside the
city on vacant lots near the Porte de Vanves, the Porte de Versailles, and the Porte d'Orléans. Before the fine weather came, the
capital was being spring-cleaned. I thought of Antoine, as I
climbed up towards the Liège metro above the St. Lazare Station.

In the wet twilight a lady in Red Cross uniform was proceeding
with ruthless authority to restore the shelter to its former condition. The beret which covered her grey hair had four stars on it,
and on her cape were the insignia of the Legion of Honour, the
Croix de Guerre and another decoration, but her rank of district
officer could clearly be read in her looks. The authority which her
rank conferred on her in the hierarchy of militarized philanthropy
had moulded her features and diminished her femininity.

Indifferent to the rain, she stood at the entrance to the station,
directing a squad of men in Red Cross uniform, who were bringing blankets and mattresses up the stairs from the underground
and piling them into a lorry. A group of North Africans, four of
them, their coats soaking wet, motionless and silent, watched her
with bright black eyes.

'Now then, don't block the way,' she said, 'or else come and
help us.'

'Tell us, madame, where can we get a bed tonight?'

'At the Porte de Vanves.'

They began to argue with one another in their own language, without budging.

I suddenly caught sight of Antoine on the opposite pavement, wearing a grey overcoat too small for him. He saw me, crossed the road and smiled shyly.

'Well, here you are at last. You've come at the right moment.'

He had known since the morning that the shelter had been condemned. The Emmaus crew had already removed the blankets lent by the Rochester. The straw would be got rid of tomorrow, by some Marines from the barracks.

'But Bruce and Lucienne and the others don't know yet. They'll be arriving soon. Then what will they do? And all the wretched crowd who come to sleep here every night? I'd rather not be here at 8.30. Come on.'

He went towards the underground stairway, and I realized he wanted to show me how he had lived during the last few weeks.

'Where are you going?' cried the lady officer.

'I was in charge of the shelter,' said Antoine quietly. 'I've left some belongings there,' and he started off downstairs without waiting for a reply.

The corridor which had been made into a dormitory formed the landing between the two stairways, one of which went up to the street, and the other down to the platform. Below, the passage of trains entering the station from Clichy or St. Lazare made the ground tremble and sent buffets of hot air in our direction. Mattresses covered the steps and the platform.

For a month past, this corridor had been alive. Men had hidden there from their anguish and had found safety. Antoine tried silently to make me realize this. He smiled a distant smile as he moved between the heaps of straw, on which the impress of the bodies could still be seen. Men from the Red Cross were removing the last of the rugs and piling them up near the stairway.

Suddenly he stooped down. 'Here is Achmed's cigarette

lighter,' he said. He picked up some crumpled newspapers, some bottles, which he put into an iron container, and a heap of blood-stained rags.

'One of the chaps was wounded,' he said, 'perhaps with a knife. He did not dare to go to a doctor—for he wasn't supposed to be in Paris. Lucienne looked after him every evening and changed his dressings. Look, here is his bowl, and Jean's suitcase.'

Near the stairway were two stools. There they spent the nights on watch, beneath the hurricane lamp, he and Lucienne the nurse, caring for the sick and preparing sandwiches to be distributed in the morning. They used to talk at length in low voices, while the refugees slept on the straw, the men on the left, the women on the right, while Bruce, the English philosophy student, mugged up his lectures on the stairs and the police played cards in the ticket kiosk. All around were posters offering the prosperity of a civilization created for the comfort and luxury of the privileged, and, flanked by these, people with hardly a shirt to their backs had to sleep. 'Delights of springtime in Corsica.'

'Let's go,' said Antoine.

The footsteps of the Red Cross men taking away the last of the bed-coverings died out on the stairs. We were alone in the depths. On the bottom stair, Antoine turned to look at the last of the posters, showing a floral clock.

'We had long discussions about that floral clock, Lucienne and I,' he said. 'Look here, you're clever, can you prove to me the existence of God by means of that sundial?'

I looked at him, surprised.

'By the movement of the flowers towards the sun?'

I was tempted to reply: 'I'm not so clever as your friend Lucienne,' but I restrained myself.

Antoine, still smiling, began to blush. The blood flowed into his cheeks. He lowered his eyes and murmured: 'She tried. Come on, I'll introduce you to her later.'

Night had fallen, and it had stopped raining. The lady officer of the Red Cross was standing by the lorry ready to go. A big

fellow, bareheaded, black hair stuck down on his forehead by the
rain, wearing a beige raincoat, a brief-case in his hand, said to her
with a strong English accent:

'Who gave the order to break up the shelter? Where will these
poor chaps go?'

The group of Arabs had approached with two women, one
very old, some middle-aged men and a family with two children.

'I don't have to explain to you,' said the lady, 'and anyhow, are
you French?'

'No, I'm English, but I've been working with the refugees . . .'

'Well, go and have a look at London. The poverty there is
worse than in Paris.'

She turned her back and got into the lorry next to the chauffeur.

'To hell with her,' said the Britisher, passing his hand across
his forehead.

'Let it go, Bruce,' said Antoine, 'the order has come from the
police. The Abbé Pierre can do nothing. A lorry from Emmaus
came this morning. They'll go into camp at Vanves.'

The lorry went off slowly. The lady lowered the window, and
made signs to us to approach.

'To pay for their transport.' She handed Bruce some money.

Her grey eyes, fixed on our group, shone in the glare of the
lights and suddenly the mask vanished. Her true expression was
revealed and she smiled, a rapid, crooked smile, full of goodness
and pity. The lorry went off, the hand waved at Bruce, and she
cried: 'Good luck.'

'You must write about all this, people have got to know.'

'Yes, Antoine, tell me about it.'

In the little pub, he told me about the short-lived and pathetic
existence of the Liège shelter.

'You know the way everyone went a bit mad on that first day
after the Abbé Pierre's appeal. In the afternoon Jean-Pierre sent
me from the Rochester with a lorry-load of blankets. The Red
Cross people were already there with the Marines from the

Laborde barracks who had brought the straw. The police, the scouts, the voluntary helpers, all this mobilized crowd, ready as if for a celebration . . . And when night came, journalists, famous people, M.P.s—all waiting for the Abbé to arrive, so that they could be photographed with him among the down-and-outs, which might help their careers.'

The down-and-outs themselves, the kings and queens of this festivity, consisted of a hundred terrified men and women, trembling with fear and cold, brought there almost forcibly by voluntary pickers-up, or who came of their own accord when their right of asylum was publicly proclaimed. There were North Africans, trembling more violently from fear and cold than the others, who had lacked the courage to perform the only desperate act remaining to them in order to save their lives: namely, to hit someone on the head and steal a thousand francs for a meal and a bed. There was also a young rogue who had been wounded with a knife and had been losing blood since the day before: his scarf was saturated with it, and also his trousers, and he wept and cried that he did not want to go to a doctor. And there were sick folk who could not get into the hospitals, and tuberculosis cases coming out of sanatoria, without money and without work.

There were prostitutes from the Rue d'Amsterdam, old and ugly, who had lost hope of getting hold of a drunken soldier on leave, or a traveller who had missed his train. There were children from three to ten years old, and some young working families thankful to have straw to sleep on. There were tramps and unemployed, the intellectual type, neatly dressed and full of disdain and dignity, former actors, artists, writers, out-of-work bureaucrats, too old at forty-five, all pretending to be there merely *en passant*, as an experience—these were the ones that it hurt Antoine most of all to see.

And there was an old lady, grandmother to an idiot boy of ten, abandoned by his mother, from whom she could not be parted; as soon as he was put in a home, the child screamed, had fits and refused to eat. The two were alone in the world. She was

reduced to complete poverty, being unable to find either work or
shelter for the two of them. They had wandered the city for
months, the old lady and the idiot boy, tied to one another by this
attachment which was at once their curse and their only refuge.

And there was a young Breton girl who must have run away
from her family on the spur of the moment—who could tell?

They had to separate men and women. The first few nights
everyone had accepted this discipline, then the episode of the little
beast called Mark occurred. 'I'll tell you about it another time.'

At the end of his tether, Antoine kept repeating that he would
tell me about these things another time, and I did not insist.

But he did tell me about Georges, a parachutist, who had
devoted his ten days' leave from a garrison in the South of France
to helping Antoine and the others. He arrived in uniform so as
to have more authority. And about his English friend Bruce,
studying philosophy by the light of the lamp when the refugees
were finally asleep, until the first train rolled by in the morning.
And Françoise, a social worker, and a scout, and a bookseller, who
spent their days trying to find solutions to the innumerable problems of these unfortunate people, getting the latest information
from the Rochester, doing the rounds of the agencies, to find
work for the unemployed, lodging for the homeless, because the
security of a night's sleep in a temporary shelter did not solve the
real problem of these precarious destinies.

'And what about Lucienne?' I asked him.

'Yes,' he said evasively, 'she is a girl of good family. I'll tell
you about it another time. Do you know what she said? That all
this misery can be fought at long range by offering our sufferings
to God and by leading a better life. Do you believe that? Why
do you laugh?'

We went out into the night to find Lucienne.

A long black automobile came down the Rue d'Amsterdam,
and stopped by the pavement near the station, whose lights were
out.

'There she is,' said Antoine, and crossed the street.

The young girl sitting beside the chauffeur opened the door.

It's no use getting out, Lucienne,' said the boy.

She resembled her elder sister, Marie-France, but seemed oddly enough older, with a less adolescent beauty. She wore no make-up. She had chestnut hair, smooth, parted in the middle and tied behind. Her large greeny-brown eyes stared at us. She smiled, and the smile revealed her age—eighteen to twenty.

'Why, Antoine?'

'The station is closed.'

She turned to look at the entrance to the underground, which seemed deserted.

'We can't desert them,' she said. She opened the door, placed a rubber-tipped stick on the pavement, and slid down from the seat. She was a cripple, half-paralysed in the legs from polio. She marshalled five or six of the waiting people into the car, and went off with them to Vanves, or to her own house, or to some other shelter.

We gave money for the fare to Vanves to the ones who were left behind.

'Come on, let's go,' said Antoine. 'All this makes me feel ill.'

But at that moment, an old woman, carrying a suitcase and dragging a child by the hand, crossed the street. The boy was an idiot, with prominent eyes and open mouth. He gave a sort of joyous neigh when he saw Antoine.

'What's this—it's closed?' The old woman could not take it in. 'What are we to do?'

Antoine put his hand in his pocket and gave her the only thing he had left: the key to his hotel room.

8

NOTRE DAME DE LA BUTTE

THE TENT on the Butte disappeared a few days later. The first of all the welcome centres, it had accumulated too much hope since the 1st of February, had vibrated to a life too intense. It had become rooted in the soil of the Butte. The cellars beneath the tent were not an anonymous passageway, like the corridor of the Liège metro. All winter the team who looked after the tent had worked at their underground, excavating the staircase and two mysterious crypts, one Romanesque dating from the seventh century, and one Gothic from the sixteenth, which probably connected with the church of St. Etienne du Mont. With pick and shovel, they had disengaged from the clayey mud of centuries the old stones of the vaulting, the walls, and the floor tiles. In the upper crypt they had set up their kitchen and their meeting-place, and in the lower one they had erected a kind of chapel. On the altar they had placed a plaster statue of Our Lady. A lady had given it to Jérémie. Neither he, nor Alain the former pub-owner, nor Robert who sold fountain-pens from a tray, nor Charles the Jockey, was very devout, but they had been determined to put the statue of Our Lady of the Poor of the Butte in the Romanesque crypt, on an altar made of a plank laid on trestles. Only one of the staff, Monsieur Edouard, the former business man, prayed regularly, morning and evening, before the statue, but some of the others, including a few of the women, came occasionally. But all the toughs of the team knew that Our Lady was there, under their feet. They felt that their benevolent work was approved and protected by that presence, just as it was by the portrait of the Abbé Pierre in the kitchen.

On February the 20th, Jérémie brought the first bunch of violets, which he placed on the altar.

The Community lived thus on three levels, the tent, full with its fifty refugees every night, on the surface; the team, eating and living all day in the kitchen of the upper crypt, and Our Lady in the basement. No one suspected that this life would be interrupted. On the contrary, they hoped that a stone shelter would eventually replace the tent. There had been talk of it.

But on March the 4th a telephone call from the Rochester ordered them to take down the tent. They did not believe it, and phoned the Abbé Pierre for confirmation. But he was away. The tent had to be taken that very evening to Vanves in a lorry, and the equipment to the Quai d'Orsay station. Another lorry would be coming to take the men to Vanves.

Jérémie declared that this order could not have been approved by the Abbé Pierre, that he would not obey it, and shouted: 'The Abbé has been betrayed.'

'Yes, indeed, it is incomprehensible,' agreed Monsieur Edouard, in his small flute-like voice.

'You—shut up, or I'll break your jaw,' cried the raving colossus. 'It's you who advised the Abbé to take down the tent.'

Whereupon Jérémie went off to do the rounds of the local pubs to relieve his rage and grief.

'It's not possible,' said the rest. 'The Abbé doesn't know that they are trying to sabotage his work.'

They discussed what the removal of the tent from the Butte would mean. There, on that height overlooking Paris, the Abbé himself had planted a flag as the symbol of justice. There, on the ramparts, he had appealed to the people of the capital to join in the crusade against the horrible and the ridiculous. Gifts had flowed in as if to the feet of an altar. The unfortunates, half-dead of cold and hunger and despair, had recovered life and found comfort and a place in the society of their fellow-men. The team had not betrayed the Abbé's trust in them. They had devoted themselves day and night to their mission, distributing clothing, blankets, utensils, meals, gifts of cash. Where would these lonely, friendless, workless, homeless people go? Or these young couples, mothers of families, children who came to them every day for comfort? The team had found work for the unemployed, lodging for some, and, in accomplishing their hard task, had never thought that the tent might be closed down, although the flood of distress had indeed diminished when the great cold was over. The Abbé Pierre must build a permanent refuge in stone. It was with this hope in mind that they had cleaned out and arranged the crypts. And now today they were being chased out as if they were useless —at a word, a community whose friendships had been cemented by the long winter's wait was being dispersed.

Why this, all of a sudden? How could they be expected to accept this return to the void? No, the Abbé Pierre could not be aware of it. It was sabotage. Someone in some office wanted to destroy his work.

They decided not to obey, to oppose by force the removal of the tent, unless the Abbé Pierre came in person to confirm the order.

Alain got up and left for the Rochester or Neuilly to try and see him and plead with him for the tent.

Jérémie returned drunk. Without a word he went down into the crypt, wrapped the statue of Our Lady in rags and papers, tied it up, and came back upstairs.

'No,' said Charles, stopping him on the staircase. 'You must leave the Virgin.'

Jérémie pushed him out of the way and, when Charles tried to hold him back, hit him full in the face, rushed up the last of the steps and disappeared into the foggy street. No one followed him.

I was unaware of all this till I arrived half an hour later. This blow of Jérémie's had crystallized their anger. Our Lady belonged to them as much as anything else there. She had shared in the life of the community and no one had priority rights over her. It now seemed to them most important that Our Lady of the Butte should remain with them and share in their battle. She should only be handed over to the Abbé Pierre, the proper recipient for her.

'Why did he take her?' cried Monsieur Edouard, very excited. 'To sell her in a pub for a drink? It's sacrilege.'

But the others, more indulgent, thought that Jérémie, crazed by grief, wanted to save something from the wreck to keep as a souvenir.

'Maybe he's taking her to the Abbé himself. Who knows what goes on inside his head?'

Indeed it was very mysterious. What had decided Jérémie to seize Our Lady and remove her, protecting her who protected him?

My arrival decided their line of conduct.

'He'll give her back to you. You've known him since the first days of Emmaus. Come with us.'

We searched high and low in the bars and cafés. One barmaid pulled out a rubber truncheon from a drawer and cried: 'Let him alone—he knows what he's doing. If you're asking for trouble, you'll get it.'

Finally we found him on a café terrace in the Boulevard St. Germain, elbows on the table, alone. He was looking straight in front of him, but seeing nothing, with a bitter expression on his face. He had perhaps given up guarding Our Lady. Drink had got the better of him. Life was opening out in front of him like an abyss.

'He hasn't got the Virgin with him,' said someone.

I got out alone, and seeing him so upset was sorry for him and felt I had undertaken something wrong and useless. Let him keep her, and with her, love, and forget everything else. But no. His act of revolt must be put right, he must obey the same discipline as that to which his fellows had to submit. I sat down beside him. His anger had subsided. He smiled sadly and extended a damp hand. I spoke to him of his duty to restore the statue which must go to Emmaus with the rest of the equipment. He let me talk, stroking his beard with his large hand. The others were waiting in the car. I told him he must not betray the Abbé's trust in him. He mumbled without conviction: 'He has betrayed *us*.'

It was too absurd to be annoying.

I tried to explain that the Abbé, when ordering the dispersal of the tent, was being submitted to some pressure we knew nothing of: an order from the police, or perhaps because of the future building of the shelter in stone on the spot where the tent had stood, or perhaps the end of the lease of the ground.

'I'll give her back to you,' he said, 'to you, but no one else. You can put her back on the altar.'

He drank down a final glass of beer and stood up.

As we climbed back up the Rue Ste Geneviève, the car followed. Jérémie went into the pub where the woman had produced the truncheon and said:

'Angèle, give me back the statue.'

Without a word she went into the back room and returned with the parcel, which Jérémie placed in my hands before leaving.

'Put her back in her place and led nobody touch her. Put her back on the altar in the crypt.'

Our Lady is probably still there, for when they left and finally closed up the entrance to the crypts, they forgot her.

9

THE FALSE ABBÉ PIERRE

THE COMMANDANT showed me into his office, which was inside a wooden enclosure in a corner of the disused railway station. It was around midnight. We were alone. The voluntary secretaries had just gone home. In a corner of the office, lying on a pile of coverings like a gun-dog, was the crook, a tall thin man, wearing a green scarf. He was asleep. His hands and feet were tied with gilded curtain cords. The remains of his false beard still stuck to his swollen face. A trickle of blood had coagulated on his long nose. The cape and cassock which the Companions of Emmaus had torn off him in their rage lay on the floor covered with dust.

'I've telephoned the Abbé,' said the Commandant. 'He's coming here about half-past twelve. He'll decide if we should hand him over to the police.'

He sat down at his desk and told me the story, just as Alfred, the guilty man, a former circus hand now unemployed, had painfully admitted it after the severe punishment inflicted on him by the lorry drivers.

The Commandant had filled in the gaps from his own imagination. He was no longer indignant, and spoke with a smile as if to say: 'This is a good story. We'll keep it for the chronicles of Emmaus.'

The police had arrested four bogus Abbé Pierres in February, and, as has already been related, countless crooks all over France had collected money by pretending to represent the homeless.

Alfred had disguised himself in a hotel bedroom, helped by an
accomplice, whose idea it originally was, an astute monster who
had Alfred under his thumb. A false beard, a cassock, a windjacket, a cape. To make himself up like the Abbé Pierre, he had
fixed to his mirror the well-known photograph of the Abbé
embracing a little girl. Then the two went down into the deserted
street. The bogus Abbé went first, bent, with hunched shoulders,
leaning on a stick, as he had seen the real Abbé Pierre do at a
lecture at Courbevoie. His accomplice followed close behind.
The first passer-by came up to him stammering, 'Father,' and,
with a reflex action common just then to all France, put his hand
in his pocket.

'For my poor,' said the good shepherd softly.

The gentleman, much moved, took a thousand-franc note from
his pocket, and removed his hat.

Then an old lady who met them was overwhelmed with enthusiasm. She wanted to take the Abbé home to tell him how
much she admired him and how, in her district, she had worked
for him from the beginning, getting the gymnasium of the school
opened, despite the headmaster's opposition, to welcome, provide
beds and food for, and nourish out of her own pocket, twenty
unfortunates, who by the way had shown no gratitude whatsoever.

'Yes, yes,' murmured the false Abbé, trembling lest his beret
did not sufficiently conceal his features under the street lamp. His
accomplice impatiently strode up and down, on the other side of
the street . . .

She eventually brought out her money, together with her visit-
ing-card which, as soon as he was rid of her, Alfred threw into the
gutter.

Then, after having approached a couple who were silent and
reluctant, saying, 'For my poor,' he judged that his ignoble
game might be a dangerous one, and said to his accomplice:
'We've got 7,500 francs. That's enough for tonight.'

'Are you mad? That's only the beginning. Come on, let's go.'

And Alfred went on, sweating with fear under his cassock. He heard behind him the tap-tap of his accomplice's stick, and ground his teeth beneath his false beard with hatred.

A lorry turned the corner and the headlights lit up his silhouette. He got out of the way, flattening himself against the wall, but a voice from the driver's seat cried:

'It's the Abbé. Hi there, Father, Father!'

This was bad luck. It was a lorry from Emmaus returning from the Quai d'Orsay station after a round-up. Alfred lost his head. He hitched up his cassock and fled. The lorry pursued him. They caught him and beat him up, tied him and threw him like a parcel of dirty linen on to the iron bedsteads, chairs, and old odds and ends with which they were loaded. And here he was.

The Commandant smiled, enchanted with the story. We lit cigarettes.

'Now let's go and see if the night-watchman has gone to sleep.'

We passed into the vast Salle des Pas Perdu of the former station.

'The night-watchman keeps telling me that the place is haunted,' said the Commandant, 'and I begin to believe it—listen . . .'

A scarcely perceptible sound echoed from the far end of the dark hall, resembling a soft drum roll. The concrete ground beneath our feet trembled. The big Alsatian which the night-watch-man held by the collar began to growl and show his fangs. The Commandant pointed his electric torch towards the heap of objects piled against the wooden partition which cut the hall in two. The far side of it was a dormitory where some forty men were sleeping. A chapel and a dining-room had also been fitted up.

'Rats?' I said.

He put his hand in his pocket and pulled out a revolver.

'There are many kinds of rats. Thieves could get in between the boards or through a corner of the railings. We have to keep a good look-out. Lucky we have a conscientious guardian, eh?'

He tapped the silent little night-watchman on the shoulder.

'He's my trusty one. He has been with us since the beginning.

He was picked up half-dead with cold and hunger on a bench in the Ventemille square. He used to be a soldier in the colonies. He served seven years in the Tschad Garrison; seven years in Africa and yet he is one of those rare beings who do not drink.'

We walked past the huge heaps of objects of all kinds which had been left there during the last months through the generosity of the nation and which the refugees and voluntary workers had drawn upon in bulk.

There had been a subsidence when a lorry had tried to drive right in. Beneath the hall were the railway lines of the suburban system. At night, beneath the draughty vault, the immense heap of odds and ends seemed to acquire a life of its own. The pyramids of shoes groaned, the wood of old cupboards creaked, a bowl slipped down with a rattle, the springs of a divan suddenly gave way with a bang. A clock began to strike, a shrill nostalgic peal, a fortnight after it had been brought and though it had not been wound for years. All these objects had served their purpose, and, unlike those in a shop, had no future.

The Commandant went over to a heap of old newspapers tied in bundles, and a pile of books. He leafed through one book by the moonlight.

'To give disinterestedly is hard. It is such a new idea that it shocks our egoism. There are treasures in these books. I shall poke about in them when I have time. It would have been a pity to send a first edition of the *Génie du Christianisme*[1] to the pulping mills. I found it the other day when I was hurriedly looking through the pile. It's the same with the pictures. There may be a Corot in there. We ought to call in an expert.

'You remember that bundle of beautiful furs?' he said to the night-watchman.

'Yes,' replied the latter, 'beautiful silver-fox coats. They were put away in a chest.'

The rays of the torch penetrated to a corner by a pillar. Suddenly a bouquet of spangles, an icy brazier, a thousand white

---

[1] Chateaubriand's famous book. *Translator.*

flamelets and iridescent lightning flashes lit up, like a miniature Christmas tree. Surprised, I went nearer to it. It was a chandelier, a large chandelier, whose crystal pendants swung to and fro in the draught. They rang softly in music grown dim with the years, evoking far-off fêtes and balls.

The lamp was put nearer. The Commandant bent over and passed his hand over the fine ribs of its copper base. Then he stood up and called sternly to the night-watchman. 'Come here!'

The latter remained in the shadow, and did not come forward when called. The Commandant strode up to him, and punched him as hard as he could, twice. The other did not move or utter a word. The dog first growled, then barked.

'Get out!' said the Commandant. 'I'm chucking you out!'

Pushing him by the shoulder, he dragged him into the office. The other let himself be pushed around. His breath came gaspingly.

This all happened so quickly that I did not grasp what it meant. I thought the Commandant had suddenly gone mad. We reached the office. Alfred had not moved.

The Commandant emptied the watchman's pockets. His nose began to bleed; he sniffed and passed his sleeve over his face. His booty was wrapped in his filthy handkerchief: twelve pendants from the chandelier. They shone beneath the lamp, pure as water, and threw glittering reflections on walls, ceilings, and on our faces.

'You idiot!' said the Commandant. 'You thought I wouldn't spot it. But a week ago I began to notice that the pendants on the chandelier were getting fewer. I counted them.'

He turned to me.

'He plucked the chandelier every night, like taking the petals off a flower. Why? Did you want to sell them?'

'No,' said the watchman. 'I wanted them for myself.'

There was a silence. The Commandant shrugged his shoulders. 'Go and wash.'

The man went out.

'There you are,' said the Commandant, with a dreamy ironical smile, his hand on the pendants. 'He longed to have these for his own.'

The sound of muffled knocks shook the wooden panels which separated the hall from the courtyard of the station. The dog, lying at the Commandant's feet, began to growl.

'Who can this be? Perhaps the Abbé.'

It was the Abbé Pierre, followed by Jean-Pierre and Domino. His voice was a whisper. He seemed worn out, as always after his lectures, huddled within himself, frail inside his heavy black cape. He passed one hand over eyes that were bloodshot from the foot-lights in the hall where he had been speaking for more than two hours.

'I'll warm you up some coffee,' said the Commandant.

'No, thanks . . . How are things going? We think we have reached the point where we can begin to transfer our staff to the depot at Bougival. The lorries will be here at six. As regards the things to be sold, we must arrange them in lots as soon as possible.'

'They can start selling them off in eight days.'

'Good.'

His glance rested on the crystal pendants of the chandelier. The door creaked, and the watchman appeared on the threshold. He did not move, his eyes fixed on the Abbé whom he was seeing for the first time. Alfred in his corner, hardly distinguishable from his coverings, still slept.

'Come in,' said the Abbé.

'This is our night-watchman,' said the Commandant.

The man came forward. The Abbé smiled, held out his hand, looking him straight in the eye as he always did.

'What's your name?'

'Justin,' stammered the poor fellow.

The Abbé noticed his untidy state, and smiled.

'Have you surprised any thieves? Has anyone tried to force the railings? I am continually being told of thefts in our depots. You must be very careful of course, but these probably occur during the daytime. But how does one prevent them? One can't search the men who have been working all day stacking the stuff, when they leave at night. How many men have you?'

'Forty,' said the Commandant.

'They've never had anything of their own, so these things in such profusion may tempt them.'

'Yes,' said the Commandant, 'and while we are on the subject of thefts . . .'

He looked at Justin, saw his terrified expression and was silent.

'Yes, the thefts,' pursued the Abbé. 'If we had waited for impeccably honest workers we should be waiting still. But I would like to ask you to make your men understand that if they want something, they must ask for it. All these things have been given for those who need them most. For the deserving, for families, not for drunkards.'

'Yes,' said the Commandant.

'This afternoon,' continued the Abbé, 'the men in charge of the clothing distribution at the Porte de Versailles centre told me that a North African, wearing only a shirt, had appeared four times running to get a jacket. The fifth time he was recognized. He'd sold the first four jackets to the old-clothes man on the corner. He came back into the queue, and the money he had made had been sent straight away to his family in Constantine. What can you do? You can't let this man go off in only a shirt. But you can't let yourself be cheated.'

'No, you can't be made a fool of,' said the Commandant looking at Justin. He threw him the dog's lead. 'Go and do a round,' he said. Justin went out.

The Commandant went towards Alfred, who was still asleep. 'This is the man,' he said, touching his feet with his boot.

The other let out a groan, opened one eye, and helping himself up with his elbows, reached with difficulty a sitting position. His swollen face, covered with blood and dust, bore traces of the blows on forehead and cheekbones, and the half of his false beard which was left gave him an expression both fearsome and comic.

'The Abbé Pierre,' he muttered.

The Abbé stepped towards him and gazed at him for a long time.

'It's odious,' he said, 'to steal in the name of the homeless. Don't you realize that?'

'Yes.'

'You had no work?'

'I was a circus hand. I've been unemployed for six months.'

'Here are his papers,' said the Commandant. 'They seem to be in order.'

The Abbé sighed.

'Is this the first time?'

'Yes, Father. I swear it.'

'Those cords must be hurting him. Take them off.'

When Alfred was on his feet the Abbé went up to him and looked him in the eyes. He pointed to the frail chest with his finger, touched the dirty scarf, as if he wanted to assure himself by contact of the quality of the heart beneath, and to what degree he could trust the man, and at last he said:

'Have you a driving licence? I am going to trust you with a car, but not for you to disappear in.'

Turning to the Commandant he said: 'Give him a windjacket, and, Alfred, go and wash yourself. You're to be my chauffeur.'

We went out into the courtyard of the station where the little Citroën was waiting. A shadow emerged from behind a pillar and drew near. It was an elderly man with a moustache and white close-cropped hair, wearing a tight grey overcoat. He had a black felt hat on his head.

'I want a word with you, Father.'

His voice was small and genteel like his person.

'Yes?' said the Abbé, his hand on the door-handle of the car.

'I apologize for speaking of this. It's about a horse, a bronze horse, which I gave.'

'Yes?' said the Abbé.

'I want to know what is to be done with it, because I attach a certain value to it, I must confess.'

'Do you want to take it back?' said the Abbé.

'No, no—I just want to know what is to be done with it.'

'A bronze knick-knack? It will be put in a sale or sent to the factory to be melted down.'

'Melted down,' whispered the small voice plaintively.

'Melted down,' repeated the Abbé.

Suddenly his voice became animated.

'Listen. Do you know what they will probably do with your horse? Make taps from it, taps for the houses at Plessis-Trévise. If it weighs ten kilograms, we can make taps for fifty houses with it. Running water is important for housewives.'

The little man stepped backwards, and bowed stiffly and cere-moniously.

'Thank you, sir,' he said.

He went off, crossing the pavement with a step made firmer by the acceptance of his sacrifice.

10

MADAME N. AT VANVES

ON WAKING Madame N. remembered a discussion she had had with her husband the previous evening. To their daughters, Marie-France and Lucienne, speaking in the rather cold voice which made his employees tremble, he had said:

'We can do nothing for that family of mental deficients. It is the business of the State and of special organizations to look after them. Their problem goes beyond the scope of individual charity. In any case, charity does not resolve the problem of social injustice. You try to drag a few wretches out of their squalor one day, but the next they dive back into it again.'

The girls had protested: 'Now that the Abbé's appeal has roused the public conscience, no social problem will remain unsolved. There's enough money and goodwill.'

'A drop of water in the ocean. The need is endless. As to the human conscience, it's already getting tired, it's going back to sleep. Haven't you noticed it? It's only normal that it should. You cannot for ever breathe the rarefied air of the 1st of February. It has become a problem on a State level. But the Government does nothing. Not much in fact is necessary: a decree, a new law, or simply the implementation of existing laws. The United Nations Charter proclaimed the right to work of all men, the right to eat. But where is it applied?'

'What is to be done then?' asked Marie-France. 'Must we leave these unhappy people in distress, till they rise up and force the Government's hand?'

'You ought to realize that poverty kills the feeling of revolt, and that it brutalizes men. Go on with your work by all means, but don't expect to change the world.'

And he quoted the phrase of Clemenceau: 'The real revolution will come when Christians start living their faith.'

Madame N. had taken no part in the discussion. She had held aloof from the movement to which her children and most of her friends had devoted themselves. She was not really hostile; she was sceptical and indifferent.

She heard the door of the flat bang. Marie-France was leaving for the office. Lucienne stayed in bed till midday. A confused feeling of sadness came over her. What about this mentally retarded family of which Marie-France had spoken the previous evening: could nothing really be done for them? Maurice Renaud the father, wounded in the 1914 war, and a devout Catholic, had married out of pity and a sense of duty a dumb girl, sweet-natured but without will-power or initiative. They had had two mentally deficient children, and had taken on two other incurables which the asylums had refused to admit. They all lived on Maurice's disability pension. Evicted as a result of the sale of the block of flats in which they lived, they were now under canvas at Vanves. These unadaptable people could not be abandoned to the city of tents, where their chronic anxiety and their inability to join in the community life might cause them new torments and provoke all kinds of setbacks and difficulties. But if the Abbé could not find them a shelter, what then?

Madame N. thought for a moment of her friend Miss Deck, chairwoman of a benevolent society committee. During the 1914 war the two young women had busied themselves with refugees. Miss Deck was one of those virtuous Anglo-Saxon women for whom charity is above all a condition of moral perfection. Her blonde hair was going grey, she wore a perfectly fitting uniform, she had a high but rigid idea of her mission and could not help thinking that if these poor people found themselves in a mess it was because they had infringed some rule of good behaviour.

People said Miss Deck was a noble soul, but she lacked that which alone bridges the gap between the helper and the helped—love. True charity is the effective hatred of all that hurts one's neighbours.

Madame N. knew all this, but she decided to take a chance, and telephoned Miss Deck.

'People from the Abbé Pierre?' There was doubt in Miss Deck's voice, even a kind of hostility towards poor people from a rival concern. 'Are they at least legally married?'

'I imagine so.'

'You're not sure? We only deal with legally married couples, but we can place the children.'

'They won't be separated.'

'That type of person is very difficult. Find out about that and ring me back.'

But Madame N. did not telephone Miss Deck. She could imagine only too well the tactless questions, the clumsy psycho-analytical examinations which the Renauds would be made to undergo to 'normalize their psyche'.

'After all,' she said to herself, 'what business is it of mine what happens to them? There are social workers for this kind of thing. They'll find some solution in the end. Lucienne's trouble is enough for me.'

A few minutes later there was a telephone call from her friend the Countess.

'Jean has not been home for three days. He's vanished with the car.'

'I expect it's only a boyish escapade.'

'No. It's not what you think, unfortunately. He's going through the same sort of "charity crisis" as your girls. That's what worries me.'

She described how the men from Emmaus had put up some tents in the park near their home, and how she had remarked that it was shameful to see such a sight in Passy.[1]

---

[1] A fashionable quarter of Paris. *Translator.*

'That was all I said, but my son looked at me with a terrifying expression and said to me, his mother: "You are wicked." Then he went out. I saw him cross the avenue and talk to these people, and then go to the garage and take the car. I am sure he has gone to offer his services to the Rochester, and that the car is being used to transport some tramp or other, or else broken cooking-stoves. God knows what state it will be in when he brings it back. Will you ask Marie-France to have a word with him when she sees him?'

Madame N. promised. As she hung up she reflected that no one could say that she was a hard-hearted woman. She had never disapproved of her daughters' devotion to the cause. She understood that poverty was something intolerably real. But her husband was right: even if we gave all our time, our wealth, our strength, we could not by helping a few people change a state of affairs which had always existed. It was a job for the Government, not for individuals.

She went out to do her shopping. As the motor-car bore her along she kept thinking of the Countess's words 'charity crisis'. That had been spared her. She had passed on the other side that hysteria which had shaken France in February. She had known sudden conversions among her friends which had astounded her. One of her old friends, rich, debauched, cynical, who believed neither in God nor the Devil, and who had lived, hitherto, only for his own pleasure, had gone on the 1st of February to offer his services to the Abbé. He had put his car, his house, and a large sum of money at the disposal of the movement. Sons of her friends, futile young zanies, now spent their nights, not in dancing in cellars and getting drunk, but in welcome centres, sorting out gifts that had come in during the day. Some were Communists, in reaction against their middle-class environment. Disobeying party orders, they had joined the movement as volunteers. She had heard sceptics who had rejected Christian dogmas saying: 'This is the real religion.' Several friends, mentally lazy and full of fears, searching for a meaning to their lives, and to life itself, declared to her that they had discovered an infallible justification in this activity: one rose above one's own problems by consecrating oneself to the service of others.

Two or three times a week Madame N. played bridge with her friends.

'You've been very distraite lately,' said the Countess.

It was true that some days she had paid less attention to her game than to her companions at the green table. She seemed to herself never to have properly examined these partners, never to have really listened to their talk. For, despite the rules observed by serious bridge players, these ladies talked a great deal as they played: about the Abbé Pierre's activities, for instance.

'It's causing an upheaval in society. We'll soon be forced to give up our beds to convicts.'

'After all, poverty existed long before all this. People didn't make such a fuss, that's all.'

'I let myself in for it at first, till I saw pairs of shoes being given to tramps who went and sold them for drinking money.'

'All this uproar has been the work of a priest. What is happening to religion? That business of the worker-priests was bad enough.'

Madame N. looked silently at her friends, one by one, and felt she was seeing them for the first time.

'We're heading for revolution.'

'Who was it said: "Injustice is preferable to disorder"?'

Madame N. felt nauseated as she listened, and admitted that their prejudices and selfishness had also been her own. Her ears smarted. She repeated to herself: 'It's true, one can't go on living like this as long as the Renauds and their four children are living in a tent at Vanves.'

'The Abbé is going too far.'

'My husband rightly says that it's just a quick flare-up and then finish. An M.P. friend has assured us that the high-ups are keeping an eye on the movement. All it needs is to deprive him of his trump card, his popularity.'

'And what about this loan for the Emergency Cities? It would be easy to wreck it if the banks refused to take part.'

'As for the law requiring one per cent of the reconstruction budget to be spent on charitable enterprises, that will never be enforced.'

At this point Madame N. got up, to the accompaniment of a surprised silence, and left her friends without saying a word. She was determined to put right this business of the Renauds as soon as possible.

At the end of February when the Paris shelters were closed, the biggest camp yet for the poverty-stricken was set up on the edge of the capital where the road for the joyous South begins. At the Porte de Versailles and the Porte de Vanves, the refugees—more than ten thousand men, women and children whom Paris had rejected—were parked in tents, like a prisoner-of-war camp. A few days after setting up the tent on the Butte Ste Geneviève, at once insufficient for the influx which arrived seeking shelter, the Abbé Pierre had arrived here on a cold night with icy rain, in a lorry with three companions. He had produced a tent and put it up with the help of electric torches on land belonging to the Public Assistance, and in the face of that organization's refusal. It was on a deserted stretch of land above the ruins of the old fortifications, behind the great proud buildings which bordered the boulevards. Some patrolling policemen on bicycles gave them a hand.

As soon as that first tent was up and the ground under it covered with straw, the Abbé had gone off in the lorry on his nightly round-up. The tent was full the first night, and the next night ten other tents capable of holding 450 persons housed 641 unfortunate people. There were thirteen babies from two to five years old lying side by side, there were mothers, with or without the fathers, with mites of under two years of age. One of these babies had inflammation of the ear, and nine women were pregnant. The team, managed by Robert and Fernand, set up the urns for each family.

The camp became a city with a reception office, a mobile kitchen, an infirmary, social services. Two huge 'squad tents' sheltered the bachelors' dormitory and 200 North Africans.

While all France was talking about them, these people, the celebrities of the hour, lying on their straw in their temporary dwelling-places, the tents, were not thinking of turning the world upside-down. They did not know they were the objects of indignant discussion. The silent weary mothers, with their children sobbing beside them, the young pregnant women, did not think of the future, while waiting for their husbands to come home from work. It was raining outside, and they were sheltered for the moment. They had received gifts of clothing, social workers had written up their cases for the files, but they were still afraid of being put back on to the streets. They were not even envious of the rich who watched them from behind the curtains of the big houses. Their spirits dulled by the constant daily worries, they thought only of elementary needs; to be less cold, to eat, to preserve their children's health, to be together, husband and wife. Bitterness had used up their energy. How could they dream of a better world? This resignation of the poor was the great victory of a bourgeois Devil.

The Renauds lived in one of these tents. The frightened children hardly ever left it. They were afraid of the other children in the camp who formed gangs and would have captured them and ill-treated them. Maurice, sitting on the straw, dreamed and prayed, did some reading, and caressed the head of a big boy of fifteen who sometimes sighed and groaned without visible reason, like a baby. The slow rainy days went by thus, in solitude and silence.

Madame N. went several times to the camp, got to know the Commandant, the social workers, the doctors, the men and women who had not gone through 'charity crises' but did their work as an ineluctable task, without sentimentality or protestations of virtue. She realized she had gained the friendship of

Alphonse, the big jovial cook of the mobile kitchen, when he said: 'The first time I saw you I took you for a tourist, because of your fine car.'

'Now you are one of us' was implied. Madame N. was proud to be accepted as one of the friends of the camp, but decided next time to leave the car on the boulevard and approach the camp on foot.

At night, while the camp slept, the tourist agencies who organize the 'Paris by Night' excursions now pampered their clientèle by showing them first the night-clubs, and then the Abbé Pierre's poor.

For a fortnight Alphonse did not get to sleep before 1 a.m. He had to serve meals for the new arrivals whom the lorries brought in till after midnight. Then he had to clean his saucepans and put out his fires. In the morning, he had to be up at six to get coffee for the men going off to work. Alphonse was fed up. He declared, and it was true, that he had lost 30 pounds in weight. The skin of his double chin hung loosely on his dirty collar. His prominent eyes were bloodshot with smoke which the wind blew back in his face. He had no time to change or wash. He had to listen to complaints about his bad cooking, and to put up with the unwillingness of his helpers, the water-carriers, the vegetable-peelers, the storekeepers. But tourists were too much. Two days before he had attached little importance to their visit. Thinking he was speaking to journalists or officials, he answered their questions politely; one lady inquired if he had been to prison. He just laughed. Then during the day he thought about it, and consulted his friends and Jérémie.

And when the coaches arrived Alphonse, armed with his soup-ladle, Jérémie and five others with batons and iron bars, were waiting for them at the entrance to the camp. The guide came forward to try to bribe his way in.

'Here, boys, here's 2,000 francs for you.'

Bang came Alphonse's soup-ladle on the guide's head. The

sensation lovers regained the inside of their coach as fast as possible and drove off into the night.

'You were a fool to hit him,' said Jérémie. 'You should have asked for 10,000 francs, then we could have bought chocolate for the kids, and a few drinks for ourselves.'

11

THE COMMUNITIES GO ON

DURING THE winter months the Emmaus communities had grown and multiplied. They had continued to work hard, aloof from the whirlwind fervour for the movement on the part of the Parisians, and their work had produced profits for the money invested in Emmaus. From 200 men in January, the effective number of workers had become 800.

By now the hawthorns were in flower, and the young wheat and barley rose above the centre of Pontault, isolated in the plain like an island in a sunny sea, green and yellow. From morning till night the cement-block machine thudded away in its shed, and houses rose up in the former wilderness. At Plessis-Trévise, round the former villa of Madame Sans-Gêne[1] which housed a community of women, the biggest works were in full production—the 1st of May would see the completion there of the first section of emergency constructions. And while along the road the walls of the cities-to-be rose before the eye. At the far end of the wooded property the clearing gang were advancing through the undergrowth, scythes in hand. The bulldozer followed them, growling, smoking, with the savage energy of a colossal wild boar, and pushed its steel snout into the earth to pull up tree roots.

On the island of Bougival, in the shade of the great willows, between the Seine, where the wherries passed, and the canal which supplies the Machine de Marly, fifty men were putting in order a ruined factory which was to be a repository, painting it red and

[1] Napoleon's laundress and mistress. *Translator.*

black. But the ragpickers who were working the muck-heap of the Bordes farm cursed the return of the heat. Waves of stench and swarms of flies rose from the manure-heaps where sometimes plants grew.

In the forest of Pomponnette, the families who had priorities for houses at Plessis-Trévise counted the days. The Abbé had promised that by the 1st of May they would be living in a solid building.

At the Réserve, and at the gas factory, new buildings in brick and wood were going up for the men, and warehouses for the goods. Jacques and his team had acquired some prefabricated huts which had been put up at the Poplars, where Jean-Pierre centralized the transport service. The foundation house at Neuilly-Plaisance knew once again the calm of former days—no lorries unloaded there now. The grass was returning to the lawns where for years there had been tents, and which the ragpickers had dug up. Down the walks of the Park could be seen only the maintenance men from the office, and priests wishing to enter Emmaus.

The Parisian offices were transferred from the Rochester to a building in the Rue du Bourbonnais.

From the trees of Emmaus, seeds had flown to germinate in the forests and the countryside of Seine-et-Oise, Seine-et-Marne, and further still; following the pioneer example of Emmaus, men had formed building groups elsewhere.

A large stretch of ground had been acquired at Noisy-le-Grand and thither were transported the families from the camp at Vanves, into a city of tents, while awaiting the building of fibro-cemented shelters.

In mid-April I met Silvio at the new offices. He was still driving round in the old Berliet, his heart and soul in the affairs of Emmaus.

'See where they're sending me today—to Fontainebleau for a load of stuff, then to St. Germain to fetch back some tents, then to transport some huts to Noisy-le-Grand. And while I am doing all this what are the office boys getting up to, eh?'

He knew quite well that he was being unjust. The office staff, the brains of the huge organization, centralized and shared out the work, playing a rôle of primary importance to the whole. A telephone and a typewriter are as indispensable as a lorry, a shovel, or a ragpicker's hook.

'Yes, I know,' he said in conciliatory tones, 'and I'm sorry for them being shut indoors all day.' Then he burst out laughing.

I asked him if he had heard anything of Antoine.

'He's back,' he said, 'working as a ragpicker at the Bordes farm with Jacques. I've just asked Jean-Pierre to let me have him back with me on the lorry.'

'Why did he leave? Where has he been hiding?'

'I have no idea,' Jean-Pierre said. 'The first time it's forgivable; even twice, but the third time . . .'

He thought for a moment, then said:

'But I'll keep an eye on the boy and stop him making a fool of himself. Next week we begin moving families from Pomponne to the houses at Plessis-Trévise.'

The opening of the Emergency City had taken place on April 30th. But the impatience of the families had run ahead of the plan. When the Minister and the Abbé and the journalists had arrived to declare open the first fifty cottages, they found them already occupied. The tenants had been there for several days. They had not been able to wait for the plaster to dry, and from the 25th of April, in the rabbit hutches of Pomponne, agitated women had begun to pack clothes, men to take down stovepipes and fold up iron bedsteads, children to pick up their few toys from the four corners of the camp. Some had hired pushcarts from the shopkeepers at Chelles, others had asked neighbouring farmers to lend them their buggies. And for fear the Camp Commandant might refuse to let them leave before the agreed date, they loaded the carts at night as silently as possible. It was a clear spring night and the forest smelt of lilies of the valley and fresh moss.

This secret exodus in the moonlight was prepared for as for a
celebration. It was impossible to quieten the children who sang
and danced as they carried their meagre treasures out to the waiting
vehicles.

Those privileged families who had lived at Pomponne from the
early days and had put their names down first for the houses did
not want their luck to cause jealousy in those who had to wait
weeks longer, or even months. But in fact, no one slept in the
camp, neither the officials, nor the 'next time' families. One after
the other, fathers and mothers got up to give a hand to those who
were leaving.

The children screamed with glee when the lorry drove up to
the wooden cabin with its corrugated-iron roof.

The family had sorted out and assembled their possessions in old
wicker trunks, boxes and bundles. Clothes, washbowls, hurricane
lamps, empty jampots, tools, humble knick-knacks—a framed
picture of St. Sulpice, a blue vase, a small china cat. All this bric-
à-brac was collected near the fence, at the foot of a young apple
tree in flower, which spread its pink-and-white branches towards
the setting sun. Those things which were not even worth giving
away were burnt. A little fire of rags, straw, old pictures, strips of
lino, was burning behind the house, and the smoke rose up in the
still air.

We loaded the lorry with beds, mattresses, the stove, the table
and chairs, a small wardrobe.

'Mind—it's not strong, I made it,' said Gaston, Luce's father.
'We came with not enough to put on the back of a bicycle, and
little by little, with what we have bought, plus what Emmaus
has given us, and what I've made, we've become like other people,
a normal family, so to speak.'

Objects, like people, help to make up a family. They are
reassuring, they protect, give comfort and pleasure.

The loading was finished. The mother took a last look round
the empty cabin. Some neighbours came to say good-bye, and

among them Marcelle, Silvio's girl, for whom he had promised to return in a week's time.

'Get the kids on to the lorry,' said Gaston, 'while I put out the fire.'

It was late that night when we got back to Emmaus.

PART THREE

BITTER-SWEET FRUITS OF PITY

THAT HARLOT PITY

'I MUST SEE you,' wrote Antoine. 'My mother died in August in Brest. I've returned to Paris. I don't know if they'll have me back at Emmaus. I left without letting them know. Write to me care of Grégor's mother, you know the address.'

His mother was dead. He had known for a long time that she could not live, but while she was alive he did not feel alone in the world. He told me later of that empty summer month on the burning stones of the quays of Brest, and of his wanderings in the rain in atrocious solitude beside the sea, of his attempt to stow away on a ship leaving for Africa, or South America. And at the same time his nostalgia for Emmaus. He could not make up his mind to emigrate.

One day he saw a Berliet lorry like Silvio's, stationary in the deserted street. He got into it and drove off. He thought what a handicap his secret malady had been to him, how ashamed he was of it, how he craved friendship and longed to be able to talk about it to someone, but how he had told no one. Emmaus had given him friendship, but there had always been this other thing which no one suspected—they had thought he was an occasional drunkard. Fortunately the fits were rare, one every two months. He could feel them coming on. He would shiver and his hands would shake, and successive and ever more violent waves of pain break over him. It would be grand to confide in someone. Silvio, perhaps, or even Lucienne. He thought of her, and Grégor's mother, and all his friends, and when the lorry ran out of petrol he abandoned it and hitch-hiked to Paris. There he went straight to Adèle. Adèle, a chic mature woman who ran a very profitable beauty-shop, had once tried to pick Antoine up at a night-club. In his state of misery and exhaustion he now submitted himself to her 'protection'.

'I'll ask the Breton to take him back again at Pontault,' said Jean-Pierre, 'but I know we cannot rely on that boy. He sticks to us because he's got nowhere else to go.'

'No,' I said, 'I think Emmaus will save him, is saving him now.'

A few days later at Pontault the assistant Commandant said to me, shrugging his shoulders:

'Antoine came back yesterday. We took him back, of course. The first time this happened he worked for a fortnight. Let's hope he stays longer this time. I give him three weeks,' and he added with a disillusioned expression: 'Yes, we've taken him back, he and many others, because of this harlot Pity.'

'Father, you and your harlot Pity have made some prize blunders.' That was how the phrase had first been used, and it had since become famous within the Community.

The Abbé had replied: 'We don't want to use men simply for the maximum financial profit to the Community. We want to give them the chance to renew themselves, and to start with a clean slate. Of course we take risks. Emmaus has been built up on just this risk.'

The thunderstorm died away. We were in the office of the community. The rain pattered down on the iron roof. In the next-door office, which was the Breton's, we heard shouting.

'I'll kill the bastard!' cried someone with a strong Spanish accent.

The accountants and architects had stopped working. The Commandant must be sitting at his desk, motionless, sharp-eyed, mouth shut in a cold silent smile, before the gesticulating man, who was exasperated by his calm.

'I'll kill the bastard!'

The Breton had seen other enraged men coming into his office, one of them armed with a knife to kill him. He had disarmed them by his silence, his hard, fixed Breton stare.

One day, in the dining-room, a drunken North African had struck one of his comrades. The Breton had intervened and knocked out the drunkard. Then he returned to his office. He knew the other would follow him, and had not locked his door. He waited for him, unarmed, sitting down, 'just to see what would happen', because he liked taking risks.

The door had suddenly opened to reveal the North African, swaying on his feet, his knife open in his hand. The Breton did not stir. He looked at him for a space of five seconds, then said: 'Ahmed, am I unjust?'

The man, his face covered with blood, had at last whispered: 'No, you are not unjust.'

The Breton stretched out his hand, and the other placed the knife in it.

'Go and get washed, and then go back to work.'

'Yes, Chief.'

'That harlot Pity.' One does not always get away with it so well.

'This on the other hand is a matter of some importance,' declared the assistant Commandant. 'It happens every day. This Spaniard works in the next village. Our Gaspard has stolen his wife. This woman trouble always ends the same way: the wife comes back, the husband gives her a beating, and the two men go out and get drunk together. The nuisance this time is that the Spaniard belongs to a group which has already given a lot of trouble.'

Little Louis went over to the large board giving the complete list of staff of all the communities, which occupied the whole of the back wall of the hut. Below each community workshop name, La Pépinière, le Bourget, Pomponnette, etc., was a row of tickets bearing the Christian and surnames of the 500 men who worked there. This list was altered every day, and every day, despite the departures, grew longer. On the right of the panel there was a space for future workshops. Tomorrow a team would go out to work over Fontainebleau, and one to build at Chaville. I examined the huge board pricked with yellow tickets, like fields already covered with the harvest, originating in a single grain. On this board Antoine's name had been put back two days before.

Standing in front of the board, little Louis pointed to one of the tickets and asked: 'Do I remove Gaspard?'

'If I had any say in the matter—yes,' said the assistant Commandant gruffly. 'But the Breton will take him back once again, all because of this harlot Pity, and once again will get into trouble for it, as if he enjoyed it.'

Beyond the barrier and the wall which closed the entrance to the community one could see the line of pavilions with green roofs of the city built by Emmaus, and on the roadside a red caravan, the last of them. Two years before, this caravan, with some tents and an old railway carriage, sheltered fifteen ragpickers and five families, in the middle of a wild stretch of bushes. At the entrance to the piece of land, at the roadside, stood a board, showing the plan of the future city of thirty buildings. Now the thirty buildings rose above the cleared ground, and the board had become a museum piece. Its Utopia had been realized. It had its place of honour in the Emmaus exhibition which toured the chief towns of France.

I thought of this, and of the first dozen or so pioneers who had worked with bare hands, of those who cleared this plot of ground, thanks to whom Emmaus had kept its promises. I thought of the beginning, of grandfather Saury, of Daniel and Kurt and their long, terrible, lonely winter; in order to keep themselves warm inside the caravan which was being shaken by icy blasts, all they could find to put in their stove were minute lumps of coke, which they picked up from the tarred surface of the road.

·   ·   ·   ·

The Spaniard's voice grew calm. The Breton was cutting short his words with brief answers.

'You know Gaspard,' said the assistant Commandant, 'that charming young rogue, crazy, doing a thousand idiotic things without meaning to, and always promising to be good in future. You know the type, capable of splendid things, but with no staying power. Not bad at heart. The Breton has a weak spot for such types—until the day when one of them will stick a knife into his stomach. We showed Gaspard the door for the first time last September after a fight. He returned in December, and was taken back. He worked hard at the cement-block machine. A fortnight later the Breton entrusted him with a lorry "just to see". He drove perfectly for a fortnight, then, having been sent to Paris to take delivery of some rolls of barbed-wire, he returned three days later, saying that the shop had not delivered the goods. Later on, he confessed to having sold them and spent the money on women. He offered to pay it back out of his wages. He was kept on. And now this third business, and it will not be the last. I hope that if the Breton decides to keep him he will send him to work in the refuse dumps.'

We set off together for Bouquet. Behind the hedge lay the immense workshops. A bulldozer ploughed up the ground with its steel point, opening up the trench where the future road would be laid. Wearing rubber sheets or light overcoats, the Companions were drilling the foundations, others were laying the iron bars holding up the rough-walling of the floor on the low sub-basement wall. Perched on ladders or straddling the metallic framework, other workers were bolting the small beams of the roof. Wheelbarrows, carts and lorries carried away to the far end of the lot sacks of cement, planks, canalization pipes, enormous cesspit cisterns. Tubes of green indiarubber, suspended from poles, carried water for mixing with the cement from one house to another. The future village was pulsating with life. The only vestige of the time when the place was nothing but grass and bushes was the shack of the Old One standing on its bit of ground.

I said: 'Well, well, the Old One is still there?'

'No way of getting rid of him,' said the assistant Commandant.

Near this unexpected cabin with its weatherboarding and corrugated roof, a goat, tied with a cord, was munching the grass. The chimney pipe passing through a hole in the wall was smoking. Emmaus had offered to rehouse the old owner in a new house with all modern conveniences. He had refused to leave his small plot on which a modern house could have been built for four families. In the middle of the noise and animation of the workshops, the miserable hovel stood in all its senile stubbornness. It said 'No' to Emmaus.

'He is too old to move!' I said.

'Don't be too sentimental about him. It's a question of money. It was agreed that in addition to a new house with four rooms, we would compensate him for the cabin and the goat with a larger sum than the ground is worth. First of all he accepted. Then, when we came to settle up, he demanded twice the amount. Meanwhile, he had been visited by the boys of a political party hostile to Emmaus, and an article appeared in a paper accusing us of evicting him from his home, a defenceless old man. There the matter rests for the moment.'

Cement dust enveloped the workers on the cement-block machine. I recognized Antoine by his striped jersey. The mixture of dust and sweat gave him a greenish-coloured, old man's mask, cracked and wrinkled. The cement discoloured his hair and hurt his eyes. He saw me, smiled briefly, and went on with his work.

The machine made 1,200 to 1,500 cement blocks per day. It functioned from dawn till dusk. On its rhythm depended the rhythm of the work in general. It was the master organism, the heart of the community of builders, powerful, noble and most venerable, the tool without which the best will in the world was helpless. For bricks they no longer relied on the goodwill of the merchants. Bought on credit in November, the machine had been paid for by its own product, the cement blocks. In their spare time the boys of Pontault had made millions and sold them to building firms.

Antoine made a sign to his friend, put down his shovel, and came over to me. We went as far as the road. There we could hear ourselves speak above the rattle of the machine. Antoine spat, and regarded me gravely through swollen, watering eyes.

'So they've taken you back?'

He did not answer, but stared away down the road and across the plain, where the last rays of the setting sun were wandering over the deserted fields of stubble.

'Do you want me to ask Jean-Pierre to put you back on the lorry with Silvio?'

'No. Later on. I would rather be here on the machine.'

'Are you getting used to the noise?'

'It stops me thinking.' Then with a smile he said: 'Lucienne sent me a card from Lourdes. She says she is praying for me. She should first pray for herself, for a cure.'

'It's for you to pray for her. We must all pray for each other.'

He murmured, shrugging his shoulders: 'What's the good of prayers?'

'It means, if you prefer, thinking intensely of others, and desiring their good.'

'I agree with that. Of course I want her to get well and walk again. You think that if I want it enough . . . ?'

He seemed to wake up, to be conscious of the breath of a distant appeal. I took advantage of this to say to him: 'When Lucienne comes back, we will go together and say how d'you do to her.'

'No, no, not yet. I'm afraid of Adèle coming here and finding me.'

I was about to leave when I was transfixed by surprise: 'Casino!' It was Casino all right (this was my nickname for him), one of the two men who came and went with slow and regular steps, from the machine to the heap of cement blocks drying. They carried the wooden tray, laden with heavy bricks, put it beneath the mould, then waited, semi-comatose, for the next brick to be born.

Casino had grown fatter. He wore glasses and had shaved off his beard. During these last two years in prison, he had lost that proud look, which he had for so long preserved when he was free, despite the wine bottle and too many women.

He had been the Community's first thief, in the extremity of his poverty. He had refused to believe in Emmaus. He was the one who sneered when Mastic, with ardent brush, painted the panel representing the thirty houses of La Pépinière. Released from prison that autumn, he had returned to Emmaus, and had touched with his hands the walls of those houses, now real and in stone.

The Breton, who knew his story, had taken him on and Casino today shared in the expansion of Emmaus, with companions who knew nothing of his past, in one of the hardest jobs.

He looked towards me and hesitated. He too recognized me. I smiled, but he looked the other way, seized the tray, and went off, bent, to carry it to the dryer.

The Breton's car passed along the road, on his way to Paris to look for the couple who had run away. He thought he knew where to find them.

'And don't come back with Gaspard, whatever you do,' cried the assistant Commandant.

He did come back with Gaspard, after giving him such a beating that the hotel proprietor wanted to call the police. Gaspard himself, half knocked out, had growled: 'It's none of your business.'

The Breton had seized him, thrown him into the car next to the wife of the Spaniard, who was weeping, and brought them both back.

And so things turned out just as the assistant Commandant had prophesied: the husband beat the wife, and then went off to get drunk with her lover. Since when things have gone better with the Spanish group.

2

ANTOINE WITH THE RAGPICKERS

IN THE autumn the cement machine left Bouquet and was set up in the workshops at Noisy. Antoine did not go with it. His deep-rooted trouble seemed to have lessened during these last two months when the reverberation of the machine had mercifully created a void in his heart and mind. He no longer suffered; he had drugged himself. He worked for several weeks discharging loads at the Bordes farm with Jacques.

Although the centres at the Réserve and Bougival had become large business concerns, with shops and repair depots, the strange, primitive and difficult life of the ragpickers on the heap had not changed since the early days when the 'lord of the rubbish heaps', the first Emmaus seminarist, Yves, Bernard the engineer, Philip the Legionary, Bastien and Jérémie, had put their forks for the first time, four years before, into the rubbish at Bois-l'Abbé, today deserted. A film company was to attempt to reconstruct their life in images of epic grandeur. By the side of a road, the surface of which had been defaced by lorries, the heap of rubbish spread out into the marshy field. Masses of rags, papers, bits of iron, bottles and the detritus of the kitchen, made a small hillock in which men grubbed about with forks. Rain, snow, frost in winter and, in summer, stench and flies—this was what they had to put up with. They lived in tents at Bois-l'Abbé, their camp-beds sunk into water and mud. There were only ten of them at that time, and the fate of Emmaus depended almost entirely on their salvage work. Since that time nothing had changed in the ragpicker's life, except that at Bordes there were thirty of them and they lived in huts. Emmaus was safe but the Community refused to ask for money. It lived by its own independent economy, and ploughed back its own profits. For these men were very proud. The Abbé could not often visit them, but he thought much of them and declared that the ragpickers were the aristocracy of Emmaus. They attached an almost mystic value to their work. They were the point of departure, the origin of it all. When the builders had no more money to build and the hotel-keepers could not take a single family, and when the offices had to close, the men of Emmaus would go back and dig for their living in the mud.

'You're being romantic about it, Father,' said the Abbé's friends. 'The future of Emmaus is not there but in large-scale building.'

'Who knows what the future has in store? Providence has revealed to us the function of the ragpicker, to make us understand that poverty is never complete, and that a man who is himself society's cast-off can still save himself by means of those objects which society has also discarded.'

This terrible task demands more courage from a man than any other and sets him at grips with the most elementary problems of life. He possesses a strange power of regeneration, by his pride in not depending on anybody or anything, except rain, wind and earth. That is why the Abbé honoured the ragpickers and said they were the aristocrats of Emmaus. Sometimes, in the midst of the tasks which took him further and further away from his men, and put him in contact with political leaders and financial bigwigs, he felt the need to rejoin his pioneers in their freedom, to take up the fork, to make his retreat amid the refuse, to recover there the consecrated sense of his vocation.

'You won't solve the social problem by scrabbling about in the muckheaps,' his friends told him.

'That's another question altogether,' he answered. 'But one day I shall go down among them to write the book which I can't write in Paris.'

.   .   .   .   .   .

I sometimes went to visit Antoine and Jacques. The boy seemed calmer. He was not yet at peace but rather in a torpor of melancholy, and when I asked him whether he regretted not being on the lorry any longer, he said: 'Yes, but I don't want to go back yet.'

He seemed to be submitting himself to some sort of test.

'I've seen Lucienne,' I told him. 'She would be glad to see you before she leaves for the South, and to invite you to her house. We will go together.'

'She's leaving?'

'Yes, to convalesce in the South.'

'I wonder,' he said, 'does she ever think of me?'

One day at the end of November, Antoine seemed so vague and withdrawn that I became anxious.

'What's wrong?' I asked him.

'Adèle arrived yesterday in her smart car and wanted to take me away with her.'

'And you're afraid you'll give way?'

He bowed his head.

'You can't understand. I'm always asking myself the same question. Why am I here, in this world? What use am I?'

One day a nice-looking fellow came to sign on. For several days we only knew that his first name was André. He worked on the rubbish heap like the others and said very little. Then, as if acknowledging a fault, he told us that he was a judge. The boys, former delinquents, confided in him their stories, which he heard in silence and humility.

'We magistrates don't know much about the lives of those upon whom we sit in judgment,' he said finally. 'We are in our own enclosed bourgeois world; we judge from our own viewpoint and try to protect our bourgeois society. This period among you will have taught me that if I'd been in your shoes, I might have acted

in the same way. We condemn people without trying to fight
the causes which have made them criminals.'

The Belgian artist, who had been taken on by Jean-Pierre, came
to spend a few weeks with us. In between working on the rubbish
heap he drew scenes from the life of the ragpickers: Jules in the
kitchen, the boys in the dormitory, in the dining-room, watching
T.V. In rapid strokes he captured on paper their expressive features, the ugliness of which he accentuated. Like the German
expressionists, he had a taste for pathetic ugliness, and his large
portraits, with their hacked and twisted faces, as if drawn with a
razor, shocked their subjects.

'We're not as ugly or as woebegone as that. You'll make people
think we're all monsters at Emmaus. And that's not true.'

But he took no notice. 'The imagination of the artist can pro-
duce truths greater than those of simple reality.'

One day Jacques took me aside.

'I'm wondering,' he said, 'if it is good for Antoine to stay here
among us any longer. Yesterday he was found in a fainting condition behind the huts. He is worn out. His moods are getting
worse. He needs change and rest.'

Antoine refused to take the holiday at the foundation house at
Neuilly which Jean-Pierre offered him. The peace of the big
house, now half-empty, was a welcome change for those comrades
who were tired and overworked, or who were either convalescent
or waiting to go to hospital.

Antoine asked to go back on the lorry with Silvio. Beside his
friend in the driving-cabin the boy relaxed. He loved driving, and
changing scenes since he could not change himself. To stay in one
place got him down. Always being preyed on by some obscure
terror, he needed to flee from it rather than come to grips with it.
And each evening, when they went on their rounds picking up
the homeless, he was hoping to find, in each sad group, his friend
Grégor.

3

THE SQUATTERS

'STOP THE cars here,' said Ernest, 'it's safer. It's only five minutes' walk.'

The villas thinned out, gave place to huts and sheds. Behind a wire fence, a lamp-post lighted up a collection of iron junk, a cemetery of cars which lay on their axles, wheelless, on the yellow grass, their carcasses twisted and half-buried in the ground. Then came the blind walls of industrial buildings, and the black and red of smoke-stained iron and concrete, steel scaffolding, towers, corrugated roofs, chimneys. A few bluish lights flickered behind panes of glass. Unexpectedly, here and there in the midst of this sad and arid architecture appeared an islet of greenery, a park and a pavilion, which seemed to have been trapped by the remorseless advance of the factories. The pavilion had a square façade with three floors, and to soften its appearance the owner had added two turrets in Gothic style. The pointed roof, covered with polished green tiles, glowed in the light of the lamp-post in the alleyway. The park fence was partly broken down. There was still a wooden placard hanging from it, on which was written *Deutsche Verwalt.*

'There's to be no breaking down the fence, or forcing the locks,' said Monsieur N. in a low voice.

'Of course not,' said Ernest in feigned indignation. 'Especially not at night. We know the rules. Look, the gate opens of its own accord.'

In fact the hinges moved quite silently. Ernest entered the unkempt park in which many of the trees had been cut down. We lost our balance walking over the roots and the dead branches. The plasterwork of the wall had fallen down in lumps. Thick planks held up the left-hand tower. The shutters were closed or else hung loose. The wind banged them together in little thunder-claps of sound.

On the third floor, almost at the roof, was a hole a yard wide, doubtless the effect of bombardments during the war. This black hole in the centre of the façade fixed us with its gaze like the stupid hostile stare of a Cyclops. The big front door seemed a wide-open mouth ready to devour us, the intruders.

Ernest had halted on the terrace in front of the steps, and looking up, seemed to defy the stone monster. Like a hunter, he was dis-playing his captured game for us, and enjoyed our surprise.

'Empty for fifteen years,' he whispered. 'The owner won't repair it, and refuses to lease it or sell at a reasonable price. He's waiting for the top price which the companies who own the neighbouring factories are sure to offer him.'

'Does our architect say it is habitable?' asked Monsieur N.

'All except the tower and two of the third-floor rooms. If the inhabitants of every condemned house were to be evicted, a third of the population of this suburb would be out in the street.'

He walked towards the steps.

'Tell me,' resumed Lucienne's father, 'have you warned the owner?'

'Don't forget,' said Ernest, 'what happened on the Boulevard Ney. We did things according to the rules. The owner sent for the police and in front of the twelve families who had hoped to lodge in his empty house, he had it demolished by a team of house-breakers. He took the roof off, the floors out, and the windows, so that the building became uninhabitable.'

'Have I told you,' murmured Monsieur N., 'that my brother is a judge? Three years ago he had to try a case of squatting. Naturally he convicted the squatters. If he were to see me here! Let's go . . . with a clear conscience.'

He laughed.

And now a strange thing happened. The hole under the roof lit up faintly and then went out. A gust of wind shook the building and banged the shutters.

Ernest went up the steps, and pushed the door, which opened silently. Like those at the entrance gate, the hinges had been well oiled. He switched on his pocket torch and went through the hall and the great empty dilapidated rooms. On the wall a flowered wallpaper, discoloured by time, had been torn off in large strips. On the swept floor were traces of water. The smell of tobacco mingled with the musty, funereal odour of a place which has been a long time empty.

'Old Louis and his young men have done a good job,' said Ernest aloud, and his words resounded and echoed in the emptiness. 'They have been repairing the inside every night for the last eight days. It will probably all be ready in the morning.'

Footsteps sounded on the hall staircase and in the rays of the torch appeared the bearded smiling face of Old Louis. Two young workers followed after him.

'Evening, Chief,' he said. 'We've just put the glass into the windows of the two good rooms on the third floor.'

'Fine,' said Ernest, 'but don't call me Chief. And what about the electric light?'

'Working everywhere.'

He laid his hand on the hall switch.

'No, don't put the light on and draw people's attention outside. What about the water in the W.C.s?'

At this moment we heard footsteps in the park, scuffling over the dead leaves, and knocking into branches. Ernest put out the light.

'Who is it?' he whispered.

Everyone held their breath. Someone came up the outside steps. Slowly the front door opened.

The light from the lamp-post in the street penetrated into the hall and a shadow was outlined on the ground and on the end wall.

'Who's there?' said a loud raucous voice. And our group was lit up by the light from a torch.

Old Louis switched on the hall light. We saw a little man, bent and thin, about sixty-five years old, with a large white moustache, and skin stretched tight over sharp cheekbones. The veins in his neck stood out. He wore a red woollen scarf, a dusty old over-coat, a bargee's cap. With his right hand he was pointing a pistol at us. His gloomy little eyes, sunk in their sockets beneath thick eyebrows, passed in review each of our faces. Ernest, brief-case in hand, took a step forward.

'Don't move,' said the man.

Ernest took another step.

'I'm the head of the Committee for Homeless People. We want to lodge families in this empty house. Who are you?'

The man was silent for a moment, then gave a little laugh and put the pistol back in his pocket.

'Good God, it's really none of my business,' he said in a slow voice, full of fatigue and gloom. 'But I've noticed lights in this house for the last four days from the factory yard. I wondered what was going on in here, since there's nothing to steal. I'm the night-watchman from the factory. I was intrigued, that's all. So you're going to put people in here?'

'Yes,' said Ernest, 'and once they're in, we hope the owner will make no difficulties.'

'I see. I've been night-watchman for five years. I've often thought it was a pity to let this empty house fall into ruin. I have sometimes thought that I would install myself here with my wife and my daughter and the kids. Seven of us are living in two rooms. Think of me if you can. Good luck and good night.'

He smiled sadly, touched his hat, and shuffled out.

Ernest switched on his torch once more and held it out to Monsieur N.

'Just shine it here for a moment, please.'

He opened his brief-case, took out a slip of paper, which had on it the plan of the house and the names of the families. He searched

in his overcoat pocket and produced a piece of chalk, and on the
fine oak door of the drawing-room he wrote in capital letters:

MOUGIN FAMILY   FATHER   MOTHER PREGNANT
FOUR CHILDREN

and on the dining-room door to the right:

NICOD FAMILY   MOTHER A WIDOW
FIVE CHILDREN

He went over to the two rooms at the back:

BION FAMILY GRANDMOTHER FATHER MOTHER
FIVE CHILDREN INCLUDING A NEWBORN BABY
DOUCET FAMILY GRANDFATHER GRANDMOTHER
MOTHER   TWO CHILDREN

and so from door to door, from floor to floor, and we followed
him watching with a kind of grave attention as his dry and
resolute little hand, isolated in the circle of light, traced the names
on the oak panels, imposing on each of these anonymous rooms
the destiny for which they had been built: to protect life. In the
silence, the chalk squeaked as it passed over the polished wood.

While Ernest was writing their names on their future homes,
the families in hotel bedrooms, in tents and in hovels, finished their
packing and prepared to leave the following morning. The
mothers, overcome by their fatigue, lay down at last on the beds
beside their sleeping children, while their husbands, helped by the
Companions of Emmaus, transported their humble furniture and
bundles of clothes to the lorries waiting at the crossr-oads. Then
they all went off together to drink a final glass of wine at the pub
before closing time. The night seemed long to all of them. Jean-
Pierre had left us to join them in his small car. He had collected

three lorries at Emmaus, among them the one driven by Silvio and Antoine. Twelve volunteers had come over from the Communities to help. Jean-Pierre went from family to family supervising, so that everything should be ready by daybreak, and to find out what each family needed. For those living in hotels who had neither mattresses nor blankets, these had been brought from Neuilly, together with stoves, cooking utensils and furniture. Thus everyone would have at least the bare minimum.

The Mougin family, whose name had been the first to be inscribed by Ernest, had been living for fifteen months in a small hotel bedroom on the sixth floor. The father was a plasterer. He earned twenty-six thousand francs a month and had paid out twelve thousand for the hotel room.

In the second family, the mother was a widow. With four of her children, she lived on a small army pension in an unhealthy lean-to without windows, electricity or water. One little girl was suspected of having tuberculosis.

In the third family, the father was a gravedigger. They lived in a small room, six feet by nine. For lack of space, they had had to entrust two of their children to public assistance.

The fourth family had lived for five months in a hotel at twelve thousand francs a month. The hotel proprietor raised the price. When the father protested, he turned them out—him, his wife, and the two children. They lived in a light tent on a camping site. They could not remain there during the winter.

And so each of the fifteen families awaited the dawn as a deliverance.

The first factory siren began to sound across the river. The sky was cloudy and the wind blew in damp, strong gusts. There were lights in the cafés, but daylight was still a long way off.

The men from Emmaus, tired from their sleepless night and shivering with cold, had collected in a pub on the small square where the three lorries were waiting. They were drinking hot coffee with some of the fathers of the families whom they were going to transport at dawn. Jean-Pierre was there, also Jacques

and Silvio and Antoine, and the twelve volunteers from the
centres of Neuilly and Pontault.

Just as in the early days of Emmaus, these lonely men who had
never had a home were glad to offer to their comrades this
security, and those who had been unable to preserve their own
family happiness thus redeemed themselves. They were willing
to risk their skins and defy the world on behalf of the happiness of
those in their charge. They felt themselves invincible. They had
recovered their self-respect and their respect for others. For the
first time in their lives, and to a greater degree than during the
war, they felt they were fighting in a just cause, and this feeling
gave them enormous strength.

Jean-Pierre reminded the fathers of the rules and regulations to
be observed in their squatters' lodging: to respect the place and
their neighbours and to pay their rent regularly.

The wives came and joined them with their children, still half-
asleep, clutching their toys, and asking in sleepy voices: 'When
are we leaving, Mummy? When are we getting into the lorries?'

Madame Belin had not slept that night in the cellar where she
had been living for a year. She had not stopped thinking, crying,
and trembling with fear, while her children slept, and her husband
helped the boys from Emmaus. And when the first sirens sounded
she went out and ran to the assembly point. She dashed into the
café like a crazy woman and seized her husband's arm to drag him
from the group.

'No, Lucien, no . . . I'm afraid. There will be trouble. I
would rather stay in our cellar than go to prison or pay a fine.'

Everyone stopped talking because this same fear underlay the
thoughts of all of them. They had hidden it from each other.
Jean-Pierre had instilled confidence into them so that they had
forgotten the risks of squatting. It was true that their present
circumstances were impossible, and that they would now have a
healthy lodging and some space, while the rent which was being
offered to the owner was within their means. But were they not

running the risk of another eviction, a summons, a fine, and even maybe imprisonment? Jean-Pierre sensed that their resolution was weakening.

'No one will go to prison, no one will be evicted,' he cried. 'You are not alone, and we are no longer powerless since we are united, we of Emmaus and you. One single family can be evicted, shamefacedly and secretly. But we won't let fifteen families be put in the street without making such a row in the Press and on the radio that the owner and the authorities will have to give way, because we have the country and public opinion behind us.'

Then he described how at Nantes the whole population had risen against a landlord who had broken up the staircase and plumbing of a house with a hammer, a house which he did not occupy himself but refused to let. The Abbé Pierre had written to the Prefect and the Minister, and he had had to give way. At Ville-au-Denis, the army had left unoccupied for five years three buildings on the edge of an airfield. Fifty-two families had been put there. In Paris several big buildings which were empty had lawfully been taken over by squatters, with the help of the neighbours and with their approval. Public opinion and the authorities themselves realized that, in the face of the lack of a housing policy and the crying need of houses, this quasi-legal solution was the only one. Nobody was robbed. The owner was compensated.

The poor were no longer alone and inarticulate. They should no longer mistrust the strength which their unity gave them. The Associations for Help for the Homeless composed of lawyers, counsels, judges and politicians, understood and defended their rights in every district and locality. The homeless population was no longer, as heretofore, obliged to hide its distress in some obscure corner, it was no longer powerless, defeated, dying in silence. If need be, the thousand men of Emmaus would go to Paris and make a demonstration in front of the Houses of Parliament, proclaiming the right to live of the very poorest.

'We must stick to our guns,' repeated Jean-Pierre, 'and stay united. We must have the courage to go through with this act of revolt in the name of the law of life, this act of justice against an outworn state of affairs, against selfishness, stupidity, injustice. There are homes all over France. The day will come when the whole country will force the Government to do its duty by ensuring homes for every working family and a humane life for everyone. It is for this that we people of Emmaus are fighting, and our cause is certain of victory. We must stick to our guns, and not flinch.'

The dawn was misty and fresh. The lorries started up, full of happy children, confident men and women, and made their way towards the huge house prepared to welcome them. Monsieur N. and Ernest, with Old Louis and his team, were waiting for them. By 9 a.m. the families were in possession.

Monsieur N. and Ernest went to tell the commissioner of police, who came back with them and brought with him several police officers.

He was a tall, spare man, with an impenetrable expression and a cold eye. He made his secretary note down the names of the tenants and check their identity papers. Then he said:

'Last week one of my colleagues told me that a family of four who had been evicted came to his station. What could he do? He could not leave a young woman with a two-year-old child in the police station. He took them home with him.' Then after a moment of silence: 'Have you informed the owner?'

'Here is a letter to him, ready,' said Ernest, 'containing the offer to pay rent.'

'You realize that if he does not lodge a complaint within forty-eight hours, I cannot order their immediate eviction?'

'Yes, I know that, and as today happens to be Saturday . . .'

'We must hope that the letter does not arrive before the midday post on Monday.'

The impenetrable face relaxed in a sly smile.

At once the delighted children began to romp about in the park.

The shutters were opened, so that the front of the house seemed to be flapping its wings. The mothers were putting up window curtains. The chimneys, fireless for fifteen years, began to smoke once again.

'The Abbé Pierre will be pleased,' said Jean-Pierre.

4

THE DARK NIGHT

BY MIDNIGHT the effect of the sleeping drug had worn off and the Abbé Pierre, half-conscious, heard a knock and murmured: 'Come in.'

But there was no one there, only the wind banging the iron shutters of his window in the clinic.

He was in great pain, but he had accepted his pain as an ally in the fight, for pain is as efficacious as prayer: it is the background to prayer as music is the background to words.

'Oh God,' he said, 'how easy are bodily sufferings compared to the sufferings due to our responsibilities and helplessness. My sufferings are my own. But my words, deeds, strength, time, all belong to others. This helplessness, this isolation is far harder to endure, and the fear that things may go wrong. The work is perpetually threatened by discouragements, clumsy planning, timid leaders, lack of discipline, laziness, quarrels, drunkenness, thefts, accidents, fires, floods, illness.

'And there are more subtle dangers, lack of understanding, the hostility of hypocrites, of public bodies, rumours and slander.'

Despite his illness, the Abbé kept in touch with the Communities by telephone, letters, messages dictated on the dictaphone, reports, visits from the men in charge. But all this did not compensate for his own absence. It was so important for him to be there, to talk to people, to shake them by the hand, to exchange a word, a look, to be at the centre of things.

He prayed that Emmaus might go on without him, that one

day he might be able to retire into a monastery for prayer and meditation, that they would forget him. But at this moment how much they needed him! To be separated from them was his greatest torment.

And he prayed to be allowed to return to them, so that their years of effort should not go for nothing. 'This still young movement must surmount this trial, because one day they will have to do without me for good and all. One day all over the world we must spread a network of our "commandos", for we fight against the one enemy everywhere, world poverty. This is the fundamental, profound necessity and destiny of our work. Only when that happens can I ask God for peace and to be forgotten.'

He must have faith that God would teach them to do without him. He remembered the words of his father who was lying ill: 'As long as one is suffering one is not wasting time. What progress we make if we accept this one thought: to put ourselves quietly and simply into God's hands.'

The peace of acceptance stole over him. In the beating of his heart he seemed to hear the church bells of Fourvières, the bells of his childhood, on a fine Easter morning.

5

FICTION AND REALITY

GRÉGOR WAS dead, Antoine told me the last time I travelled with him just before Christmas in Silvio's lorry. 'His mother told me the day before yesterday. They found his body, riddled with bullets, in the Saint Martin canal.'

He made no further comment but the news had greatly upset him. Perhaps he still thought himself responsible for the death of his great friend because he had not rejoined him when Grégor ran away. It was a defeat for him and for Emmaus. He was sorry also for Grégor's mother who would never escape now from her wretched room and from her despair.

'You must put it out of your mind,' said Silvio. 'There is nothing you can do.'

We drove along the muddy roads of the Brie, beneath clouds heavy with rain. The lorry was carrying a load of planks for building new huts for the community of ragpickers at the Bordes farm. I wanted to see my friends of the Community to say good-bye. Between Antoine and myself, old Didier, just out of hospital, had squeezed himself in.

'See that light?' said Silvio. 'What is it?'

Above the sodden fields, like an enormous star suspended above the horizon, a violet-blue light went on and off and finally remained brilliantly shining beyond the bushes against the dark background of the sky, at a distance hard to determine.

The intensity of the rays and their bluish colour intrigued us and we drove in that direction, near the two rubbish dumps of the Bordes farm.

A grey car had been in front of us for some time. At the Plessis-Trévise cross-roads it took the road leading to the rubbish dumps. The road ran alongside the walls of the farm, whose buildings hid the strange light from us.

The car, bouncing about in the muddy ruts, slowed down, parked itself up close against the white wall, and a familiar bearded face leaned out of the window.

'It's the Abbé,' cried Antoine. 'I want to talk to him.'

'No, it's not,' I said. 'Keep calm.'

'What? It *is* the Abbé, isn't it? I've wanted to talk to him for so long . . .'

He was beside himself, and I suffered at the thought of his forth-coming disillusionment.

Silvio drove the lorry abreast of the car.

'Is this the way to the Bordes rubbish dump?' cried André Reybaz.

He recognized me at once. Behind his beard his face lit up in a smile. When he smiled no one could think he was the Abbé Pierre, for the Abbé's smile was quite different. Perhaps the Abbé's smile had had the same young spontaneity when he was André's age, but the last fifteen years had involved him in too many struggles and too many dangers. Now the Abbé's smile was rare, and therefore more precious.

A bearded and filthy group of ragpickers, wearing tattered denims, stood on top of the refuse-heap. They had forks in their hands, and iron receptacles, sacks, and baskets in which to put their pickings.

White with cold beneath their beards and their filth, they looked more real than real ragpickers. They were not working, but were waiting for the order to work. These ragpickers were preparing to scratch among the heap, but the Community would not benefit greatly from anything they harvested in their iron receptacles. None the less, they were working for Emmaus, to defend and prove the worth of Emmaus. There was not a single genuine ragpicker among them. The real ones had stayed on the other heap on the edge of the forest near their camp, two hundred yards away. Not one of them had come over out of curiosity. They had their day's quota to do. For them, all this business of Press, radio, cinema, this publicity going on around Emmaus, was just mirage. They had broken with the vain 'glories' of this world.

The rubbish dump was given over to the film people. Producers, directors, assistants, cameramen, technicians for sound and lighting, stumbled about in the débris. The huge projector whose light we had seen afar off was now turned off: it stood on a nine-foot-high scaffolding. The camera, on its big wheels, stood on rails which sank into the heap of paper, rags and jampots. Electric cables wound about through the débris to end up at the sound vans and the generator truck parked on the edge of the road with the cars belonging to the film people.

'Look here!' stammered Antoine, wide-eyed. 'Isn't it the real thing? Why isn't it the real Abbé Pierre?'

I told him that when the Abbé had agreed, reluctantly, that a film should be made, he had said: 'The life of our Communities must not be disturbed. We ourselves could not pretend to do what we have done in actual fact. The actors and technicians can come among us and learn our ways. And I hope they will try to understand us and make others understand what sort of life we lead and what Emmaus really means.'

But Antoine did not seem to understand what I was telling him. His haggard gaze fixed on the group of actors whose silhouettes were outlined against the gloomy sky. He repeated: 'They're not real ragpickers. They're in disguise.'

The director, standing beside the camera, raised his arms and cried: 'Silence . . .' then: 'Sound. Please stop that engine on the road.'

Silvio obediently switched off. A young man arranged the rod on which the microphone hung above the actors' heads, and the big projector was turned on. A flood of cold light fell on the players, accentuating their dishevelled appearance.

The men, isolated in the ray of artificial sunlight, motionless in the filth, seemed to be dummies composed of the same matter, rags and mud. The director had put Reybaz in the middle of the group, close to the camera, facing a big fellow wearing a dusty bowler hat. Through a gap in his vest his naked chest was visible.

Then I realized that they were making that scene which I have described in another book: about the team of ragpickers, on the day when they first came to work the rubbish dump, and had come up against a genuine rubbish collector. Just as a fight was about to start, the Abbé Pierre had appeared.

'That's a nice tattoo you've got there,' the Abbé had said to the professional.

Surprised by the appearance of a priest as a patron of the rag-pickers, the latter had proudly undone his vest. Engraved on his skin was the sad and expressive image of the head of Christ, crowned with thorns. Above it were written the words: 'He suffered', and beneath: 'So have I.'

'That's grand,' the Abbé had said to him. 'Where did you have that done?'

'In prison.'

The Abbé had looked him straight in the eyes.

'I think we are going to understand one another.'

'I agree.'

Everyone was silent, waiting for the signal for action. All you could hear was the wind, rustling the papers, rags, and grass, and in the distance, on the road, a motor horn.

The assistants were all looking at the ragpickers outlined against the cold light, and it seemed as if homage was being paid to the boys from Emmaus whom they were personifying.

'The swine, the swine!' repeated Antoine. 'Let's get to hell out of here. It makes me vomit!'

'Shut up!' murmured old Didier. 'It interests me.'

'Doesn't it revolt you to see them pretending while you do the real thing for three hundred francs a week?'

'No,' said Didier, 'I don't care. Everyone's got his job to do, and so long as the Abbé approves.'

The young clapper-boy, carrying the ruled clapper on which was inscribed the number of the scene sequence, came in front of the camera, hiding for a moment Reybaz and the ex-convict ragpicker.

The producer shouted: 'Motor!' then: 'Action!'

'Ragpickers of Emmaus, number 329,' called the clapper-boy.

He folded up the clapper-board and got out of the way quickly. Silence, and then:

'That's a nice tattoo you've got there,' said Reybaz.

I imagined, rather than heard, these words, which were smothered by the murmur of the wind. The microphone hanging above the actors' heads picked up the sentence and transmitted it to the recording apparatus inside the sound truck.

Thanks to all these intermediaries and gadgets, a living moment of truth concerning Emmaus was going to reach the hearts of men, to remain a short while in their memories, evoking some degree of love.

When the shooting was over, I went to the dump to shake hands with friends among the actors and technicians. We were chatting when I saw Dudule coming along the road from the Community centre of the ragpickers; he was one of the real ragpickers, a small man, fifty years of age, as bewildered by life as a little child. He had lived for three years in the house at Neuilly-Plaisance and had been working on the rubbish dumps for six months. His only hope was Emmaus, the only person he had to lavish his affection on, the Abbé Pierre.

For months past the Abbé had not been available. Dudule had so much to say to him. He held a piece of paper in his hand, and advanced timidly on Reybaz, removing his cap and disclosing his bald white cranium.

'Father,' he said, 'I would like to speak to you.'

'Excuse me,' said Reybaz smiling, 'but I am not the Abbé.'

'Father,' replied the other, unmoved, 'it's about divorcing my wife.'

'But I am not the real Abbé Pierre,' answered Reybaz gently. 'I am a film actor. Look . . . I've got make-up on. I'm wearing a false beard.'

Dudule slowly raised his bewildered childlike eyes, opened his toothless mouth, and whispered reproachfully: 'Oh, Father, why do you say that? What have I done to you?'

Then, as Reybaz did not move, he turned round and went off, with bent back, carrying his disappointment with him. The only thing he loved on earth had betrayed him, like all the rest.

6

ANTOINE AND THE WEIGHT OF OTHERS

THOUGH ANTOINE had gone off in disgust after the filming incident, he had not really thrown in his hand. A commercial traveller found him unconscious on the deserted road and took him to the police of Noisy who informed Emmaus. A doctor examined him. When he came to Antoine insisted that he was drunk which we knew to be untrue. Jean-Pierre, Jacques and I had suspected the truth: through fear of being dismissed from jobs, which had happened several times, Antoine had obstinately concealed the fact that he was an epileptic. But after all what did that matter? There were men with all sorts of mental ailments at Emmaus. The only thing that mattered was that they should not be a danger to the rest. Jean-Pierre suggested that Antoine should do a quiet office job for a time, but he begged to be allowed to go round in the truck, though of course Silvio could not let him drive again.

After the heavy rains of January, the Seine rose in flood and inundated the workshop at Bougival where the ragpickers were installed. Silvio came back from Neuilly in the truck to help in the rescue of both men and goods, and Antoine splashed about for two days up to his waist in water. He had another breakdown, with an obstinate high fever. This was another sort of illness.
From the Seine-et-Oise sanatorium a fortnight later, he wrote me some letters in his childish handwriting, surprisingly full of spelling errors: he was to have an operation at Easter, in three

weeks' time: his chest had been affected and six ribs were to be removed. He was frightened by the prospect but at the same time felt at peace in the calm and isolated routine of the hospital, in the evenings enjoying a stroll in the flowery orchard, whose apple blossoms reminded him of his old home in Brittany. He thought of his comrades, of friendship, of all those fine and beautiful things which were the real substance of life. This was the beginning, he felt, of real understanding and only now was he beginning to live. The operation would be his baptism. Afterwards all he wanted was a glimpse of the sea before taking up his work again at Emmaus.

Jean-Pierre, Jacques and Silvio all visited him, surrounding him with the loving-kindness of Emmaus. And Lucienne did not forget him either. These two young people loved each other although they never spoke of this.

While Antoine was undergoing his trial, the Abbé Pierre emerged from his. Only just convalescent, he decided to go to the United States. Though some of the Community complained that he was abandoning them, most of them understood that the trip was essential so that his message could be spread everywhere; they promised to keep his work going in his absence and that they would never betray his confidence. When echoes of his successful mission reached the Community they were proud indeed—and knew that the Abbé could never forget them.

Immediately on his return to Paris, the Abbé was assailed by a multiplicity of problems. Helped by public opinion and committees formed everywhere, he organized protests against the eviction of squatters and initiated new squatting centres—more camps for homeless families right in the centre of Paris.

More than ever he felt confidence in his Community which had by no means been weakened by his long absence. When he went round the workshops the Abbé found that the enterprise, 'even if it was a little untidy, even if its knees were dirty', had grown more robust.

Centres of ragpicker-builders were opened up in the provinces at Lille, Nantes, Rennes, Evreux, Limoges, Dunkirk, Nice and even abroad in Canada and Japan (the ragpickers at the Bordes farm contributed 50,000 francs to the community at Kobe, near Nagasaki).

And how was Antoine, now convalescent, making out against this background?

Across the sunlit Picardy plain, between the ripening grain and the beetroot fields, a group of children and young people were walking slowly down the treeless road, carrying bundles of corn-flowers and poppies. The tallest of them was holding by his right hand a child who shook ceaselessly; on his left he supported a young man bent like an aged cripple, with a half-witted face; in front of him two other invalids, one of whom laughed incessantly; behind him, a spastic paralytic in his wheel-chair pushed by a dumb companion.

Light clouds hovered over the distant horizon and a warm breeze ruffled the wheat. A flurry of dust rose around the group. Silos towered over the fields, straw stacks rose up and beyond was the village with its white stone houses and slate roofs, and a square bell-tower, like the one Van Gogh painted a few days before his death. One of these houses was the children's home. These children, victims of their parents' alcoholism, of squalor and extreme poverty, for whom there had been no place of refuge, at last had a home of their own. Stumbling and shaking, they clung to this tall youth who was their leader, in their need of protection, to be loved and to give their love.

He was walking slowly, moderating his pace to that of the most crippled among them who hung on his arms with all the weight of their almost useless bodies. His own scar was hurting him, but to keep up their spirits he began to sing a Negro spiritual, *Vagabonde par le monde*, which they loved to hear.

It was perhaps the lowest ebb of Antoine's life, both physically and spiritually. But it was at the same time his point of departure and his moment of arrival. He was at least on the road. He was recovering, and Lucienne was also getting better. He too was making his contribution to Emmaus. He was not separated from the Abbé—to whom he had still never spoken, whose hand he had not yet shaken—nor from Jean-Pierre, Jacques, Silvio and the rest of us. Never had he been nearer to them.

For the first time Antoine felt really at peace and for the first time he spread peace around him. He was carrying his own burden, taking upon himself the weight of others who had at last answered his question: 'What good am I? Who needs me? Who loves me?' Antoine at last felt himself part of the living world.

Suddenly he saw a blue Citroën approaching across the bright plain. It stopped in front of the group. The Abbé Pierre got out, went up to Antoine and, smiling, held out his hand.